BRIDECHILLA
FIELD GUIDE

THIS BOOK CONTAINS OUR WHOLE WEDDING.
If found please return to ...

Name:

Surname:

Phone:

Email:

IF YOU OBEY ALL THE RULES, YOU MISS ALL THE FUN

Katharine Hepburn

BRIDECHILLA

Help grow the Bridechilla movement,
tag a #**BRIDECHILLA** and spread the word!

Join our group the 'Bridechilla Community' on Facebook to meet
like-minded Bridechillas and Groomchillas. It's the best
gosh darn wedding planning community around.

Be sure to follow Bridechilla on
Facebook @thebridechilla
Instagram @bridechilla
Pinterest @bridechillapod

ISBN 9781999916305

Design by Viktoriya Nesheva and Richard Maddock
Printed in China

First edition 2018, Happy Days Media Inc.
Second edition 2019, Happy Days Media Inc.
Third edition 2020, Happy Days Media Inc.

Happy Days Media Inc. 2020
www.thebridechilla.com

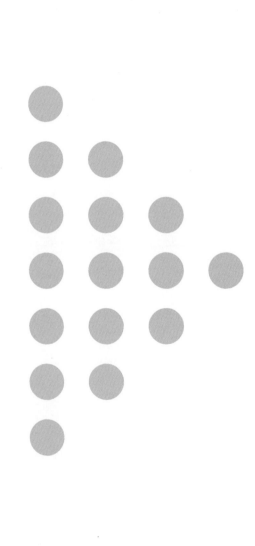

CONTENTS

MARRIAGE IS THE ALLIANCE OF TWO PEOPLE, ONE OF WHOM NEVER REMEMBERS BIRTHDAYS AND THE OTHER WHO NEVER FORGETS THEM.

Ogden Nash

What is the Bridechilla Wedding Planning Field Guide?

IT'S A BOOK OF OPTIONS

This Field Guide contains checklists and lots of handy questions you might like to ask prospective vendors.

It includes things you might like to do to plan your wedding. It's a book where you can write things down and tick them off as you go, or you can throw them in the Fuck It Bucket* to burn for eternity.

Being a Bridechilla or Groomchilla is all about understanding how you feel, knowing what you want, and learning how to communicate better to achieve your goals. It's about being organized and deflecting opinions. It's about marrying the person you love the most and having an awesome party.

This field guide is for all couples, no matter whether you're straight or gay, Millennials or Baby Boomers. Whether this is your first marriage or fourth, I know that you will find value and guidance in these pages.

I hope you enjoy this Field Guide, and if you would like to delve deeper into the wedding planning process, may I suggest you grab a copy of the *Bridechilla Wedding Planning Survival Guide* and listen to *The Bridechilla Podcast*.

Happy Days,

Aleisha

*The Fuck It Bucket is the place to discard wedding tasks we intended to do but lost interest in, ran out of money for, or realized don't matter.

What Sort of Wedding Do You Both Want?

There is a lot of bias in the wedding industry, claiming it is a one-sided day, that women are the only people interested in planning weddings and that men are only interested in showing up on the day and deciding which liquor to serve. There seems to be a lopsided projection of priorities that are repeatedly perpetuated.

However, a wedding is about two people coming together. This is a day for both of you, so start planning your wedding day exactly as you will end it—as a team.

It's about being a team, working together and planning the wedding that you both want.

That means talking to each other.

Before you plan, buy or book anyone or anything, you need to grab your partner and ask the following questions of each other.

If you've already started planning this is a great exercise to make sure you are both on track and working together to create the wedding that you both want and will enjoy.

If you're on the same page you can start the process off as a team. You don't necessarily need to have all the answers, but being a **BRIDECHILLA** or **GROOMCHILLA** is all about knowing what you want and how to communicate it.

QUESTIONS TO ASK EACH OTHER

What are both of your non-negotiables when it comes to the day? (Good photography? Perhaps you don't care for flowers but really want a live band?)

S
ceremony/reception

decorations

photography (yr do you)
- middle
grnd)

for T
not long (reception)

cost (budget)

What are the three elements that are important to you? (Atmosphere? Food? Amazing music?)

1 decorations
2 dress/makeup/hair
3

1
2
3

What do you think is a reasonable figure to spend on your wedding?

max ~8 - 10k

of 4k - 7k

How can you use your budget to create an event that will be memorable without having to miss out on things or go into debt?

- DIY
- prioritizing

- good deals
- minimize

NOTES
- reception - brides don cry
- ceremony - traditional, too much
  - bridal party debate

~ dress - rent/used

 5

A COMPROMISE IS AN AGREEMENT WHEREBY BOTH PARTIES GET WHAT NEITHER OF THEM WANTED.

Anonymous

What to do When?

TIMING IS EVERYTHING

Perfection doesn't exist; so striving for it is a waste of energy, when instead you could be drinking wine and eating cake.

Truth.

Taking risks and wedding planning are not often connected, but I think one of the keys to being a Bridechilla or Groomchilla is trusting your gut, and doing shit that lots of other couples just wouldn't do.

Being prepared for things that might go wrong is sensible, but don't allow yourself to be overcome by "what ifs."

The key to attaining Chilla status is being organized but not overwhelming yourself with obligations and things to do.

Going through the wedding planning process knowing that some people will not understand some of your decisions, and that some vendors might not be the right fit for you, is a great start. If you feel confident that you can cope with whatever comes your way and work as a team to solve any hiccups, then you are going to be A-OK.

We invest a lot of time, energy and money into planning weddings, but a wedding day is just the beginning of the adventure.

It's only one day in a long and incredible journey.

This time line is a guide only.

● Use it to tick things off as you go, but don't feel panicked or worried if your time line isn't matching our suggested time line.

There are no rules and no right answers to this schedule.

● Make the big decisions and then work through the list and decide what you need and what isn't relevant to you.

● The 'trick' to ditching wedstress and being a Chilla is knowing what you both want, being organized and not jumping ahead.

● **Let's do this!**

WEDDING PLANNING CHECKLIST

12 Months

 LOCK IN YOUR BUDGET
How much are you REALLY going to spend? I don't mean fantasy money, I mean your real, actual budget.

 DRAFT GUEST LIST
No announcements! Just spend some time preparing a big ol' list. This isn't your final list, just an initial brain dump.

 CONSIDER HIRING A WEDDING COORDINATOR OR PLANNER
I don't know how many weddings you've planned before, but having an expert on hand no longer requires a big budget and will ultimately save you time and money. Coordinators are investments. They have great contacts, and their heads are full of wedding planning knowledge. Hire one!

LOOK FOR A VENUE
The venue can dictate so many of the decisions you will make. Size, cost, decor, availability, and location are key factors to consider. Don't jump in and book the first place you find. Think it over.

BOOK YOUR OFFICIANT
This person is going to help you make it official! Take time to consider what sort of ceremony suits you as a couple. Light-hearted? Religious? A fusion ceremony of Seinfeld quotes and Psalms...hey, do what you like, it's your wedding. *Tony*

BOOK YOUR PHOTOGRAPHER AND VIDEOGRAPHER
Make sure your memories are captured by a pro. Good photographers book out well ahead of time, so don't leave this decision hanging.

SUBSCRIBE TO THE BRIDECHILLA PODCAST
This is a no-brainer—it's awesome! What are you waiting for?

NOTES

Budget - $7,500   • Gateway Catering?

Venue Options
- Ceremony - Savage Mill Deck / Reception - Carroll Baldwin Hall

- 1840s Plaza (possible Church ceremony)

- church wedding
- private hall / estate catering

WEDDING PLANNING CHECKLIST

12 Months

NOTES

NOTES

8 Months

CONSIDER CATERING

If your venue allows outside catering, now is the time to think about food! Start collecting quotes from caterers. If you have employed a wedding planner or coordinator, ask them for suggestions.

THINK ABOUT WHAT YOU ARE GOING TO WEAR

If you are a Bridechilla considering purchasing a couture or made to order wedding dress, most designers recommend a 6-8-month lead time. No pressure though, there are plenty of options that don't take as long. Suits are quicker to make, but now is the time to start thinking about what you would like to wear.

GO BACK TO YOUR GUEST LIST: CHECK IT TWICE (OR 100 TIMES)

How does that original list look? Are there people on the list that perhaps you might not actually want to invite? At Bridechilla, we call them obligation guests and ditching them is easier than you think. Check out the *Bridechilla Survival Guide* to learn how.

NOTES

NOTES

WEDDING PLANNING CHECKLIST

8 Months

NOTES

NOTES

WEDDING PLANNING CHECKLIST

6 Months

 SEND SAVE THE DATES AND PURCHASE WEDDING STATIONERY
If you are planning a destination wedding, this can be done further in advance.
Remember, if you send a save the date to someone, unless they commit an act
of friendship treason, they should be on the wedding guest list—so do not send
anything until the list is locked. — bookmarks!

BRIDAL PARTY
Perhaps you've already chosen your main people, perhaps you are going solo?
If you are having a bridal party, the 6-month mark is a great time to make it
official and start thinking about their attire and where you might need their help
along the way.

 TRANSPORT
In this wedding podcast host's humble opinion, wedding cars are one of the first
things to go if you are looking to save money and are considering planning a
more sustainable event. You don't need to show up in a vintage car or horse-
drawn carriage. Seriously. If you are having your ceremony and reception at
different locations, consider how your guests will move from each location. Are
you paying or are they?

 ALCOHOL
Will you have an open bar? Can you supply your own alcohol? Package or
cash bar? Signature cocktail or no booze at all!? Big decisions. Pour yourself an
aperitif and mull it over.

BOOK HAIR AND MAKE UP
Find a skilled person who will enhance you, someone you can work with to
achieve your desired look. Book a trial and get your gorgeous on!

DJ & ENTERTAINMENT
What sort of wedding entertainment are you hoping to provide for your party?
Live music or a DJ? A string quartet or drum and bass hero? Book them now
before someone else gets them!

 CAKE
Taste as many cakes as possible. Trust me. **THIS IS MY #1 PIECE OF ADVICE.**

✓ **GIFT REGISTRY**

If you are planning to work with a gift registry, select your items and set up the logistics. — no gifts

✓ **ADDITIONAL PARTIES AND CELEBRATIONS**

Book bachelor and bachelorette parties, weekends, extravaganzas!

START WORKING ON YOUR SCHEDULE

It is never too early to think about logistics. If you are working with a coordinator or planner, start to talk through your expectations for the timing of the day, taking into consideration the time required for setup and when you need to leave the venue at the end of the event.

FINALIZE READINGS AND WORK ON YOUR VOWS

The ceremony should be top of mind when it comes to your wedding preparations. So many couples leave this until the week of their wedding and then panic! Bridechillas don't panic. Fact. — mom sings

BUY ACCESSORIES AND ATTIRE

Shopping! Confirm the wedding attire and adjustments to be made if need be. Underwear and shoes should be purchased in the lead up to your final fitting.

NOTES

- bookmarks
  — gift or drawing?

° look up my tiny artists
— calle & others

WEDDING PLANNING CHECKLIST

6 Months

NOTES

NOTES

WEDDING PLANNING CHECKLIST

2-4 Months

RINGS!
Buy your wedding rings.

MEET WITH YOUR PHOTOGRAPHER
Your photographer is someone you are going to want to feel comfortable with. Lots of photographers like to arrange a pre-wedding meeting to go over your shot list and talk through the day.

SEND YOUR WEDDING INVITATIONS
8-12 weeks lead time is the 'new normal' for invitation lead time, but if you are traveling for a destination event, make sure you give your guests plenty of notice. Number or name all your RSVP cards. There is nothing worse than receiving an RSVP and not knowing who it is from.

REHEARSAL DINNER
Book a venue for your rehearsal dinner. Create and confirm a rehearsal dinner guest list.

NAME CHANGE?
If you are choosing to change your name, make an appointment ahead of time with the appropriate authorities to ensure you aren't waiting for millenia.

(Tyler Prubbry↓?)   Pruitt-Young

NOTES

NOTES

WEDDING PLANNING CHECKLIST

2-4 Months

NOTES

NOTES

WEDDING PLANNING CHECKLIST

1 Month

MARRIAGE LICENSE
An important document to make it legal. Don't forget it!

CONFIRM VENDORS
Make sure your vendor contact list is in order. Work through the list to confirm that each vendor knows where they need to be and when. Again, a wedding coordinator will completely take care of this for you. Seriously, hire one. You'll thank me.

MEET WITH YOUR PLANNER
Take time to meet with your venue manager, planner or coordinator to go over last-minute details, confirm your running order and hand over any jobs or errands that you can distance yourself from. Because friend, it's gonna get busy—not crazy, but busy—in the lead-up to your wedding.

CHECK RSVPs
Use a spreadsheet or app to keep track of RSVPs. Politely prompt people if you haven't received a response from them one week after the cut-off.

SEATING CHART
If you are assigning seating, work out who sits where. Some couples like to go old school and use a physical seating chart, but there are plenty of awesome online seating planners to explore as well.

BOOK IN SOME RELAXING TIME
Wedding planning can be full on, so that's why it's great to step away from plans and do something normal. Go to dinner, see friends, Netflix-and-chill your brains out.

WEDDING WEEK!
Haircut and color: nothing drastic—consult with your hairdresser on the best timing. Collect your dress and suits. Confirm final guest numbers with caterer/venue.

Breathe.
Relax.

Enjoy the love and attention.
Drink champagne...and eat cake!

NOTES

WEDDING PLANNING CHECKLIST

1 Month

NOTES

NOTES

How much money are you going to spend on this shindig?

THE BUDGET

How much have you got and how much do you want to spend? I am talking real figures here, not "If I do an extra forty-six shifts at work," or "If we each sold a kidney," or "If we won the lottery." I mean what is the real amount that you can afford without having to obtain the services of a loan shark?

No matter what your final budget is, the quickest way to get a handle on costs is to be honest with yourself about what you can spend. Not what you'd like to spend, but what is realistic. Being truthful about your budget isn't saying you must give up on what you want, it's just the first Bridechilla step in deciding what is important to you for the day and what you can cut back on and get creative with.

When you have decided on your final budget, set that as a cap and do your best to stay under it. The easiest way to do that is to separate wedding money and everyday money. If your budget is $15,000, create a wedding bank account and only pay for wedding costs from that account. Don't dip into your everyday money. It's easy to spend

a bit more here, a bit more there and blow the budget completely. There are numerous online savings accounts that are free and convenient for keeping track of spending.

Go back to your non-negotiables. When you imagine your wedding, what do you see? Is it a big lavish party? Is it a cultural celebration? Is it about great food and wine? What would you exchange or let go of to make this day match your expectations?

For example, if your "dream" dress is $6,000 and your total wedding budget is $10,000, then the reception is probably going to be limited, or you need to pick another dress.

These are big decisions and it's only the beginning. If your future husband/wife doesn't seem as enthralled by the details of the day, get them involved. If they don't seem jazzed about the turquoise and pink color scheme, it might be because they secretly loathe it. Or maybe they don't give a shit about color schemes but care about music.

You won't know if you don't ask.

IT'S CLEARLY
A BUDGET.
IT'S GOT A LOT OF
NUMBERS IN IT.

George W. Bush

THE BIG LIST OF THINGS
YOU MIGHT WANT TO BUY

Your wedding budget:

PLANNING • • • • • • • •	BUDGETED AMOUNT	VENDOR ESTIMATE	AMOUNT SPENT
Wedding planner/coordinator			
Wedding magazines			
Bridechilla Survival Guide			
Marriage preparation course			
Other			
Total:			

STATIONERY • • • • • • •	BUDGETED AMOUNT	VENDOR ESTIMATE	AMOUNT SPENT
Invitations			
Save the date cards			
Reply cards			
Thank you cards			
Postage			
Ceremony program			
Reception menu cards			
Place cards			
Guestbook & pen			
Map & directions			
Seating plan display			
Other			
Total:			

PHOTOGRAPHY & VIDEO • • •	BUDGETED AMOUNT	VENDOR ESTIMATE	AMOUNT SPENT
Engagement photography			
Wedding photography			
Videography			
Photo prints for thank you card			
Photo album(s)			
Other			
Total:			

BRIDECHILLA ATTIRE • • • •	BUDGETED AMOUNT	VENDOR ESTIMATE	AMOUNT SPENT
Wedding dress/suit			
Alterations			
Veil/headpiece			
Jewelry and accessories			
Shoes			
Lingerie and hosiery			
Manicure and pedicure			
Hairstyling			
Makeup			
Other			
Total:			

GROOMCHILLA ATTIRE • • •	BUDGETED AMOUNT	VENDOR ESTIMATE	AMOUNT SPENT
Tuxedo or suit tie or bow tie			
Accessories			
Shoes			
Other			
Total:			

FLORAL • • • • • • • • •	BUDGETED AMOUNT	VENDOR ESTIMATE	AMOUNT SPENT
Bridechilla bouquet			
Maidchilla bouquet			
Groomchilla boutonniere			
Groomsmen boutonnieres			
Parental boutonnieres/corsages			
Reception table arrangements			
Head table arrangements			
Delivery and set up			
Other			
Total:			

WEDDING RINGS · · · · · ·	BUDGETED AMOUNT	VENDOR ESTIMATE	AMOUNT SPENT
Rings			
Total:			

CEREMONY · · · · · · · ·	BUDGETED AMOUNT	VENDOR ESTIMATE	AMOUNT SPENT
Marriage license			
Venue fee			
Officiant fee			
Confetti or other			
Ceremony music/musician			
Other			
Total:			

RECEPTION · · · · · · · ·	BUDGETED AMOUNT	VENDOR ESTIMATE	AMOUNT SPENT
Venue rental			
Table and chair rentals			
Reception meal and service			
Glassware rental			
Liquor			
Non-alcoholic beverages			
Cake			
Cake-cutting fees			
Cake topper			
Late night snack/buffet			
DJ and/or entertainment			
Dance floor, lighting, PA			
Wedding favors			
Lighting			
Bartender fee			
Decorations			
Centerpieces			
Total:			

TRANSPORTATION · · · · ·	BUDGETED AMOUNT	VENDOR ESTIMATE	AMOUNT SPENT
Bridal party transport			
Guest transportation			
Total:			

INSURANCE AND PERMITS · ·	BUDGETED AMOUNT	VENDOR ESTIMATE	AMOUNT SPENT
Special occasion permit			
Liability insurance			
Other			
Total:			

FAVORS & GIFTS · · · · · ·	BUDGETED AMOUNT	VENDOR ESTIMATE	AMOUNT SPENT
Bridesmaids' gifts			
Groomsmen gifts			
Other			
Total:			

OTHER · · · · · · · · · ·	BUDGETED AMOUNT	VENDOR ESTIMATE	AMOUNT SPENT
Rehearsal dinner			
Hotel accommodation			
Other			
Total:			

OTHER EXPENSES

EXPENSE	DESCRIPTION	BOUGHT FROM	SPENT	PAID/DATE

Total spent:

NOTES

OTHER EXPENSES

EXPENSE	DESCRIPTION	BOUGHT FROM	SPENT	PAID/DATE

Total spent:

NOTES

A LOT OF PEOPLE ARE AFRAID TO SAY WHAT THEY WANT. THAT'S WHY THEY DON'T GET WHAT THEY WANT.

Madonna

CONTRACTS AND LEGAL STUFF

Once you have decided that a vendor is for you, it's important to get your agreement in writing. Until you sign a contract and put down a deposit, you have no guarantees that vendors will reserve the date of your wedding. No matter how small the business, a contract should be signed. This is a Bridechilla non-negotiable.

A contract is valuable for both parties in the agreement. It is so you know precisely what the vendor will be supplying to you and when, and how much you will be paying them to do so. A contract makes sure that both parties are aware of their rights and obligations via a written agreement. It will dictate what will occur in the case of cancelation, whether that entails a refund or an obligation on your behalf to pay the vendor regardless. A contract is just as important to the client as it is to the vendor. If you come across a vendor who says, "I'm not big enough to have a contract" or, "I can't afford a lawyer to draw one up for me," I call bullshit.

There are thousands of results for 'contract template' in a Google search. It is simple to download one and edit it as required. Yes, if you are a vendor, ideally it would be good have someone with some sort of legal qualifications to check it, but a basic contract isn't complicated and at a bare minimum should cover the points below.

What should be in a contract?

- Dates and times of all services required

- Date of the wedding

- Names of all parties involved in the agreement. Even if you have wedding donors paying, the contract is between you and the vendor.

- The deposit and final payment amounts as well as the payment schedule

- Contingency plans, for example, what happens if it rains? Will your venue provide you with an alternative space or is it up to you?

- Description of services

- Refunds and cancellation clauses

- Ownership, particularly when it comes to photography, such as social media rights and whether they can use images from your wedding for promotion etc.

- Additional charges and taxes. Is the price final? Can you add extra people to the catering bill? How much will that cost?

- Rental items, what are the costs to you if damage is incurred or items are lost?

Don't sign anything until you have read it properly. If you have questions and amendments, make them be known. Both you and the vendor should sign and date two copies.

Making Quotes Easier

The quest for quotes can be time-consuming and confusing. Here are some quick tips to consider before contacting vendors.

- Pick three vendors in each category and start from there.

- There is no point initially emailing 25 photographers. This is how people get overwhelmed with wedstress very quickly. They throw a bunch of emails out there and then start to panic when things come back over budget, or they all come back within budget and they are spoilt for choice.

- Make sure that you look at testimonials, Yelp reviews, Google feedback, etc.

- Do your research and don't hesitate to ask for more testimonials or to speak to a recent client about the services that they received.

- Know when it is appropriate to negotiate prices and when it's easier to walk away. For example, we negotiated to provide our own appetizers and dessert table. Our caterer agreed to this, which saved us a bunch of money. They were happy with this arrangement, but a lot of caterers would have told us to shove it.

- Be mindful that vendors are running businesses and have set their pricing to levels that they think are fair for their services. Not everyone price matches. Respect that and move on.

- Trust your instinct with pricing. If it feels too good to be true or you get a whiff that something is off, then move on. It's easy to find someone else.

YOU CAN'T HAVE EVERYTHING

• • •

WHERE WOULD YOU PUT IT?

Steven Wright

HIRED HELP

Organizing, planning, making lists, color coding, worrying about lists, bartering, schmoozing, reorganizing lists and writing more lists isn't everyone's idea of fun. Many people, in fact, do not like doing the aforementioned things and would rather pay a professional to avoid them altogether.

The decision to hire a wedding planner or coordinator may be a simple one. If you have a busy job, and know that making sneaky calls and emails most days to vendors and suppliers might get you fired, then perhaps hiring a wedding planner is a good option. If you feel completely overwhelmed/disinterested/sweaty at the thought of planning your own wedding, then that also might be a good indicator that you should begin exploring your wedding planner options.

Hiring a wedding planner can come at varying stages of planning. Some couples hire a planner before they have made any major decisions, others wait until three weeks before the wedding. If you are thinking about engaging the services of a planner, I recommend inviting them to help you as soon as you can.

Your wedding planner or coordinator is someone you are going to have a lot of contact with during your wedding planning journey, so be sure to spend some time to learn about their business and make sure you gel with them. You don't have to be best friends, but you do have to feel confident that this person (and their recommended suppliers and vendors) will be able to work with your budget and share your vision for the day.

One of the big secrets to being an instant Bridechilla or Groomchilla is to know your limitations, and to value your time and your money.

Time Saving Tip

"I'm in the States, and I created both a wedding email and phone number. I created a Gmail account and a Google voice number; both are free. I have the Google voice number forwarded to my cell phone. The great thing is that when someone calls the number they are asked to state their name, it then tells them they are being connected when it rings through to my phone, and when I answer it plays the recording of their name back to me and I get the option to answer or send to voicemail. All the voicemails and any text messages that are sent to the phone number end up in my email. It's a great way to screen unsolicited vendor calls when I'm at work. When I sign contracts/select a vendor, I give them my actual cell phone number. The Google voice number is great for expos! Also, I should mention they are normal phone numbers. Mine has the same area code as my cell phone number."

Bridechilla Marie

WEDDING PLANNER CONTACTS

Name:

Company:

Price:

Contact name:

Details:

Number:

Email:

Notes:

Address:

NOTES

Name:

Company:

Price:

Contact name:

Details:

Number:

Email:

Notes:

Address:

NOTES

NOTES

WEDDING PLANNER CONTACTS

Name:

Company:

Contact name:

Number:

Email:

Address:

Price:

Details:

Notes:

NOTES

Name:

Company:

Contact name:

Number:

Email:

Address:

Price:

Details:

Notes:

NOTES

NOTES

QUESTIONS FOR WEDDING PLANNERS OR COORDINATORS

How many weddings have you planned?

How do payments work (a percentage of our budget, a flat fee)?

Will there be additional expenses on top of your base fee (travel, parking, food)?

What's the average cost of the weddings you plan?

What is the typical size wedding you plan for?

Do you have testimonials or references that we can contact?

How much do you require for a deposit?

When is the final payment due?

Do we need to pay our vendors directly, or do we pay you and you handle it?

How many weddings will you be working on at the same time (day of and throughout the entire process)?

What are some challenges you have faced?

Can you work with our budget? Is it realistic?

How will you help us stay within our budget?

What sorts of services do you offer (coordination, full-service event design or full planning)?

Do you coordinate deliveries, rentals, set up times and other meetings with various vendors on the wedding day?

NOTES

NOTES

QUESTIONS FOR WEDDING PLANNERS OR COORDINATORS

Do you carry personal liability and professional indemnity insurance?

Do you handle event styling?

Have you planned any other weddings at our venue?

Are there specific vendors you like to work with?

How many people on your staff will be at the wedding?

What are some of the ways you would suggest to save money and still have a wonderful day?

How much time will you be committing to planning our wedding?

How often will you be in contact with us in the lead-up to the wedding?

How do you prefer to communicate—phone, email?

What's the best way to get in touch with you?

What if we don't gel with your suppliers? How negotiable are they?

Do we have to use your preferred suppliers?

Are you affiliated with any venues?

What is your favorite wedding or event that you have planned?

What's your secret for staying calm under pressure?

What's the biggest wedding mishap you've ever encountered and how did you deal with it?

What happens if you're sick or otherwise unable to be there on the day of our wedding?

NOTES

NOTES

The Venue

Weddings can take many different shapes: formal, traditional, religious, casual, huge, minimalistic, vintage-inspired, or even *Game of Thrones* themed (although perhaps not "Red Wedding"). The list is as long as your imagination. There are no rules, especially when you're a Bridechilla.

Your wedding is entirely your gig, and sometimes the freedom to do whatever the heck you want can be overwhelming. After spending a few minutes on Pinterest, it can easily feel like there is too much choice and have you wishing for the simplicity of the 1950s when everyone got married in a church or country club.

Choosing a wedding venue is a big decision that will shape all your plans to come, so it's not one to make in haste. However, let me remind you that it's just a place and wherever you choose to get married will be special because it's about **you**, not a ballroom or a view.

The location of your wedding will not only help shape your day, but it will also dictate a lot of decisions such as budget and number of guests.

Finding a location that can work realistically with your wedding vision is the first step to making it happen. Be open-minded but not decor delusional. Seeing an empty art gallery as a blank canvas is great, but if you wish to transform the blank canvas into something magnificent, you are probably going to need help from someone that has the time, money and skills to make it happen.

Have you the time?
Have you the skills?
If not, can you afford to pay someone who does?

Considering a non-traditional venue is a great option for couples who want to make their own choices every step of the way. Such a choice will allow you to have control of all facets of the planning process and have the flexibility and freedom to bring in your suppliers of choice without the restrictions of a traditional venue.

To help guide your venue decision, think about the timing of your celebration and what sort of food and atmosphere you want.

Weddings do not have to be formal, seated affairs with alternate drop meals followed by speeches and dancing. If that format doesn't work for you, ditch it.

You can get married at a bowling alley with sushi and a silent disco. I repeat, there are no rules. And if you do get married at a bowling alley with sushi and a silent disco I would love an invitation!

EIGHT VENUE IDEAS

1.

2.

3.

4.

5.

6.

7.

8.

I LOVE BEING MARRIED. IT'S SO GREAT TO FIND THAT ONE SPECIAL PERSON YOU WANT TO ANNOY FOR THE REST OF YOUR LIFE.

Rita Rudner

NOTES

NOTES

NOTES

VENUE SHORTLIST

Venue 1:

Company: _____

Contact name: _____

Number: _____

Email: _____

Address: _____

Price: _____

Details: _____

Notes: _____

Quote requested:

Quote received:

Price:

Site visit booked:

Shortlisted:

Venue 2:

Company: _____

Contact name: _____

Number: _____

Email: _____

Address: _____

Price: _____

Details: _____

Notes: _____

Quote requested:

Quote received:

Price:

Site visit booked:

Shortlisted:

Venue 3:

Company: _____

Contact name: _____

Number: _____

Email: _____

Address: _____

Price: _____

Details: _____

Notes: _____

Quote requested:

Quote received:

Price:

Site visit booked:

Shortlisted:

NOTES

NOTES

NOTES

VENUE SHORTLIST

Venue 4:

Company:	Price:
Contact name:	Details:
Number:	
Email:	Notes:
Address:	

Quote requested:

Site visit booked:

Quote received:

Shortlisted:

Price:

Venue 5:

Company:	Price:
Contact name:	Details:
Number:	
Email:	Notes:
Address:	

Quote requested:

Site visit booked:

Quote received:

Shortlisted:

Price:

Venue 6:

Company:	Price:
Contact name:	Details:
Number:	
Email:	Notes:
Address:	

Quote requested:

Site visit booked:

Quote received:

Shortlisted:

Price:

VENUE QUESTIONS

THE BASICS

Can the venue accommodate our desired seating capacity?

Is our date available?

What is the cost of hiring the venue for the ceremony and reception? What is the cost per head?

What is the length of time included in the booking?

What time do guests have to leave the venue?

What does the venue cost include?

How flexible are the packages and pricing?

How much deposit is required?

What are the payment options?

What is the cancellation policy?

What is included in the wedding package?

Does the price include taxes and will a service charge be added to the final bill?

Is there an additional charge for the wedding rehearsal?

Is there an extra charge for renting chairs and tables?

Is the venue available for exclusive use?

Is there an in-house wedding coordinator?

Do you have a one wedding per day policy?

Are there any planned building works or renovations before the wedding date?

Can we have the ceremony and reception on the property? If so, what is the changeover plan for converting from ceremony to reception?

What are the possible options in case of inclement weather?

Are there any preferences for suppliers/is there an in-house caterer?

NOTES

NOTES

VENUE QUESTIONS

Can we meet with the chef prioir to our wedding?

Are kitchen facilities available for use?

Is a complimentary menu tasting included?

Can we bring our own alcohol?

Can we bring our own cake/other food items?

Is there a late bar? How late will the bar be open?

Is there a charge for a bar extension?

What are the alcohol choices in the package and what are the upgrade costs?

Do you have the option of a paid bar?

Is there a specific amount that has to be reached before the end of the reception?

Are there any additional charges for bar staff or waiting staff?

What time is the meal served?

Do you cater for special dietary requirements?

NOTES

NOTES

VENUE QUESTIONS

SET UP AND DECOR

What time can we gain access to the venue for set up?

Is the venue being used to host a funtion the day/evening prior to our booking?

What time do we have to leave?

What are the guidelines for decorations?

Can you store decor items for us prior to the wedding?

What crockery/cutlery/linen is provided as part of the package?

Are there different table (shape, size) options available?

What, if any, decor is provided?

Can we hang drapery or other decorations?

Can vendors deliver goods prior to access time?

NOTES

ENTERTAINMENT, SOUND & LIGHTING

Are there noise restrictions?

Where does the band set up?

Do you have a space for the band to base themselves in between sets?

Do you have a dance floor?

Do you have a sound system with microphones for the speeches and adequate speakers, or do we need to hire them?

Can we connect an MP3 player, phone or laptop to your sound system? If so, what cords or plugs do we need?

What in-house lighting does the venue have (if any)?

Are there any restrictions to adding lighting to the venue?

Can we visit the venue after dark to plan our lighting?

NOTES

NOTES

VENUE QUESTIONS

ACCESS AND LOGISTICAL DETAILS

Is there easy access for the elderly and disabled?

Can we get ready at the venue? If so what time can we have access?

Is the venue child-friendly?

Is there a car parking area for guests and is it complimentary?

What are the bathroom facilities?

Does the venue have public liability insurance?

NOTES

FINANCIAL

What deposit is required?

Are there any other fees we should know about—corkage, taxes, service charge?

What's the cancellation policy?

Is there a payment schedule?

When do we need to confirm final numbers?

Are discounts/packages dependent on certain numbers of guests booking accommodation?

Are there special reductions for off-peak e.g. weekdays or winter?

NOTES

NOTES

Catering

Depending on your venue, the decision of who caters your wedding may already be made for you. In-house catering can be excellent as it's one less vendor to hire, but also be sure to do your due diligence and try the food prepared on-site before signing a contract and ask all of the questions about catering requirements and any special requests.

Finding a wedding reception venue that welcomes outside catering for many couples is a dream as it gives you the freedom to do as you please. If you are lucky enough to secure one of these gems, make sure that early on in the process you acquire all of the necessary information about what you can and can't do on the property.

Use word of mouth and testimonials. Do they have good reviews? Check sites like Yelp, Google, TripAdvisor, and Zagat. Search for images on their social media accounts of events that they have catered before and, of course, meet with them and sample their fare.

Consider the type of food that the caterer produces and your needs and wants; for example, do they serve vegetarian, vegan, or gluten-free options? Are they open to working with you on designing a menu for your wedding, or are they strict with their menu choices?

When hiring a self-catering venue, the onus can be on the couple to arrange the rental of catering components such as glasses, crockery, platters, tables, table linen, chairs, etc. A wedding planner or coordinator can work with the caterer to make this happen, but this will often be at an additional cost to the catering budget. Check with your venue about these details as some will hire these additions in-house; others will require you to bring your own.

If caterers are supplying crockery, etc., make a note of replacement fees for broken items and check with the rental company if you are expected to return the crockery and glassware clean or rinsed.

I JUST DON'T WANT TO LOOK BACK AND THINK, "I COULD'VE EATEN THAT."

Anonymous

CATERER QUESTIONS

Have you ever catered an event at my venue?

How will the food be prepared at my wedding?

How many weddings have you catered before?

Can I see reviews or testimonials from couples?

How many events will you cater on my wedding day?

Can we choose the menu from scratch or do you provide set packages?

Will you provide tableware, cutlery or table runners? Can we see them set up in advance?

I've got _ people to feed and _ much to spend, can you work with my budget?

Have you catered for this many people at one time before?

What options are there for potentiall reducing the bill?

What happens if we cancel or change our wedding date?

What's your policy on refunds?

How many other weddings do you plan to cater for that week?

Will you be catering any other weddings on the same day as ours?

Will it be you doing the catering or other members of your team?

What happens if you are unwell on our wedding day?

Will you provide your own serving staff? Is this included?

What is the server-to-guest ratio?

When do we pay for the catering?

Are there deposits and payment plans?

Is tax included in the quote?

When do you need to know final numbers or menu choices?

I've got guests with many different dietary requirements – how will you work with that?

Will you print our wedding menus for us? Is this included in the price?

How far in advance do we need to book our wedding caterers?

How many tastings can we have? Are they included in the price?

At what point do the menu tastings take place?

What is your policy on tipping – should we reserve money for tipping the waiting staff?

How do you present your dishes? Can we see examples?

Where do you source ingredients?

NOTES

NOTES

CATERER QUESTIONS

What style of dishes and dining would suit my venue?

Am I choosing the right kind of dishes for the time of year?

Do you have any particular specialities that we should try?

What are the alternatives to the traditional buffet?

We love laidback barbecues and hog roasts – can you cater for these?

Who is handling rentals?

Do you need us to hire in any equipment?

How much space do you need (if cooking in a marquee, for example)?

Are canapés included in the price?

Can you also make my wedding cake?

We want a cheese wedding cake – can you supply it?

Can you supply alcohol too? How much choice do we have for this?

What menus do you offer for children?

We need to feed our photographer too – how much will you charge for their meal?

Our wedding is early in the afternoon so we'll need food again later in the evening – what options do you offer?

Will you include tea and coffee after the main meal?

QUESTIONS TO ASK AT THE TASTING

Is this what the portion size will be?

Is this what the dish will look like?

Will you be preparing this dish any differently on the day of the wedding?

How long will we have to finalise our menu choices?

Where do you source your ingredients?

NOTES

NOTES

Alcohol

Depending on your venue, you may be offered a choice of beverage packages, which range from full-catered, all-inclusive bars to bring your own booze.

When considering alcohol packages, you should start by looking at your guest list. How much you see alcohol playing a part in your day and celebrations? If you are organizing a dry wedding it might not play a part at all.

Do you have pregnant guests, older people, non-drinkers, lots of kids attending?

Do you plan to have a longer function where you will serve alcohol through the entire celebration?

Do you want to serve spirits, beer, and wine?

Will you be creating a signature cocktail?

Perhaps you are keen to serve cocktails and then move on to wine and beer?

Do you have specific labels or brands of alcohol that you wish to serve at your wedding?

Finalizing these details will help you decide the best package for your day and what works for your budget.

NOTES

TOO MUCH OF ANYTHING IS BAD, BUT TOO MUCH CHAMPAGNE IS JUST RIGHT.

F. Scott Fitzgerald

Questions to ask your bartender or venue about alcohol service:

Can you help us calculate alcohol amounts for our event?

Can you describe a little bit about how you run an event while bartending?

How many hours will the bar be open?

What time will the bar close?

We're having _____ people at our event. How many bartenders do we need to make sure the wait for drinks isn't too long?

What is the cost to hire an extra bartender?

What is the typical bar setup?

Do you supply glassware?

Can we see samples of the glassware?

What are the various packages that you offer?

Do you charge a set fee per person, or by the amount of alcohol consumed?

What are the rates for sodas, bottled water, and juices?

How will we be charged for opened bottles of liquor?

How will bartenders handle intoxicated guests?

If the caterer or venue is providing alcohol, can you provide proof of a liquor license and liability insurance?

How will the bartenders be dressed for the event?

What do you think of our signature drink? Can you make it?

Can our guests order shots?

Will bar staff bus tables?

Do you work with our favorite liquor? If not, can you supply it?

What's the tipping protocol?

What type of insurance do you have?

VENUE: _____

ALCOHOL NOTES

VENUE: _____

VENUE: _____

DRINKS SHOPPING LIST

WEDDING BOOZE BREAKDOWN

Our breakdown is based on 100 guests at a 5 hour wedding on a summer evening.

100 guests—5 hours

1 Bottle of Wine = 4 Servings	1 Beer = 1 Serving	1 Bottle of Liquor = 16 servings

Option Wine & Beer: 70% Wine, 30% Beer

    7.5 Cases of Wine (12 Bottles per Case)
    2 Cases of Sparkling (Recommendation: Prosecco or Cava)
    2 Cases of White Wine (Recommendation: New Zealand Sauvignon Blanc or Steel Aged Chardonnay)
    1.5 Cases of Rosé (Recommendation: Dry, Provence Style)
    2 Cases of Red Wine (Recommendation: Meritage/Red Blend or Cabernet Sauvignon)
    150 Beers
        Pale Ale Style and a Darker Option

Option Wine, Beer & Light Bar: 50% Wine, 20% Beer, 30% Liquor

    5 Cases of Wine (12 Bottles per Case)
    2 Cases of Sparkling (Recommendation: Prosecco or Cava)
    1 Case of White Wine (Recommendation: New Zealand Sauvignon Blanc or Steel Aged Chardonnay)
    1 Case of Rosé (Recommendation: Dry, Provence Style)
    1 Case of Red Wine (Recommendation: Meritage/Red Blend style or Cabernet Sauvignon)
    100 Beers
        Pale Ale Style and a Darker Option
    10 Bottles of Spirits
        3 bottles of Vodka
        3 bottles of Gin
        4 bottles of Whiskey

Option Wine, Beer & Full Bar: 40% Wine, 20% Beer, 40% Liquor

    5 Cases of Wine (12 Bottles per Case)
    2 Cases of Sparkling (Recommendation: Prosecco or Cava)
    1 Case of White Wine (Recommendation: New Zealand Sauvignon Blanc or Steel Aged Chardonnay)
    1 Case of Rosé (Recommendation: Dry, Provence Style)
    1 Case of Red Wine (Recommendation: Meritage/Red Blend style or Cabernet Sauvignon)
    100 Beers
        Pale Ale Style and a Darker Option
    16 Bottles of Spirits
        4 bottles of Vodka
        4 bottles of Gin
        4 bottles of Whiskey
        2 bottles of Rum
        2 bottles of Tequila

NOTES

ALCOHOL SUPPLIERS

Vendor:

Company:

Contact name:

Number:

Email:

Address:

Price:

Package:

Notes:

PAYMENT DETAILS	Date 1		Paid	Date 2		Paid

Vendor:

Company:

Contact name:

Number:

Email:

Address:

Price:

Package:

Notes:

PAYMENT DETAILS	Date 1		Paid	Date 2		Paid

Vendor:

Company:

Contact name:

Number:

Email:

Address:

Price:

Package:

Notes:

PAYMENT DETAILS	Date 1		Paid	Date 2		Paid

THE ONLY WAY WE WILL SURVIVE IS BY BEING KIND. THE ONLY WAY WE CAN GET BY IN THIS WORLD IS THROUGH THE HELP WE RECEIVE FROM OTHERS. NO ONE CAN DO IT ALONE, NO MATTER HOW GREAT THE MACHINES ARE.

Amy Poehler

Bridechilla
Bridal Party

IF YOU'RE WORRIED....

... about cost and potential dramas, or you're not into having a girl or guy crew, then ditch them all together. It's as easy as that. Or, if you have one particularly close friend, pick them. Or have 35 people—it is completely up to you.

Whoever you choose to have with you in preparation for your wedding, they are your A-Team. They love you, you love them, and they want to share the day with you and vice versa. Your wedding day will be amazing because they will be there beside you, clinking glasses and dancing like maniacs at the end of the night.

Remember that your wedding preparations are but a short moment in your life and these ladies and gents will be there long after the confetti is swept away. Yes, it's your day, but trust me, if everyone around you is having a brilliant time and enjoying themselves it is so much sweeter. Bridesmaids have been given a bum rap recently. When did these close friends

go from ladies who turn up to the church on the day in a nice dress (exactly what our mother's bridesmaids perhaps would have done) to pre-wedding slave friends—emotional punching bags that organize everything from strippers to destination getaways? Sure, you aren't that type of bride, you are a Bridechilla, but the devolution of the bridesmaid has been swift, and I think rather brutal.

Bridesmaids, your maid of honor and groomsmen are people who you both can rely on to help you out, to plan a great bachelor and bachelorette party (if that's your style) and placate any wedstress.

Enjoy this time with them and keep up the communication!

*If you are looking for an excellent Bridesmaid gift, then may I suggest our Bridesmaid Guide, *The Maidchilla Manual*- it's basically this book for Bridesmaids!

NOTES

BRIDAL PARTYYYY

Name:

Number: Alterations:

Email: Pick up date:

Address: Notes:

Size: Shoe size: Height:

Bust: Waist: Hips: Dress ordered   Paid

ITEM	IDEAS		WHERE TO BUY/RENT	BOUGHT	BUDGET	SPENT
Attire						
Shoes						
Accessories						
Alterations						

Name:

Number: Alterations:

Email: Pick up date:

Address: Notes:

Size: Shoe size: Height:

Bust: Waist: Hips: Dress ordered   Paid

ITEM	IDEAS		WHERE TO BUY/RENT	BOUGHT	BUDGET	SPENT
Attire						
Shoes						
Accessories						
Alterations						

Name:

Number: Alterations:

Email: Pick up date:

Address: Notes:

Size: Shoe size: Height:

Bust: Waist: Hips: Dress ordered   Paid

ITEM	IDEAS		WHERE TO BUY/RENT	BOUGHT	BUDGET	SPENT
Attire						
Shoes						
Accessories						
Alterations						

NOTES

BRIDAL PARTYYYY

Name:

Number:

Email:

Address:

Size: Shoe size: Height:

Bust: Waist: Hips:

Alterations:

Pick up date:

Notes:

Dress ordered   Paid

ITEM	IDEAS	WHERE TO BUY/RENT	BOUGHT	BUDGET	SPENT
Attire					
Shoes					
Accessories					
Alterations					

Name:

Number:

Email:

Address:

Size: Shoe size: Height:

Bust: Waist: Hips:

Alterations:

Pick up date:

Notes:

Dress ordered   Paid

ITEM	IDEAS	WHERE TO BUY/RENT	BOUGHT	BUDGET	SPENT
Attire					
Shoes					
Accessories					
Alterations					

Name:

Number:

Email:

Address:

Size: Shoe size: Height:

Bust: Waist: Hips:

Alterations:

Pick up date:

Notes:

Dress ordered   Paid

ITEM	IDEAS	WHERE TO BUY/RENT	BOUGHT	BUDGET	SPENT
Attire					
Shoes					
Accessories					
Alterations					

NOTES

BRIDAL PARTYYYY

Name:

Number: Alterations:

Email: Pick up date:

Address: Notes:

Size: Shoe size: Height:

Bust: Waist: Hips: Dress ordered   Paid

ITEM	IDEAS	WHERE TO BUY/RENT	BOUGHT	BUDGET	SPENT
Attire					
Shoes					
Accessories					
Alterations					

Name:

Number: Alterations:

Email: Pick up date:

Address: Notes:

Size: Shoe size: Height:

Bust: Waist: Hips: Dress ordered   Paid

ITEM	IDEAS	WHERE TO BUY/RENT	BOUGHT	BUDGET	SPENT
Attire					
Shoes					
Accessories					
Alterations					

Name:

Number: Alterations:

Email: Pick up date:

Address: Notes:

Size: Shoe size: Height:

Bust: Waist: Hips: Dress ordered   Paid

ITEM	IDEAS	WHERE TO BUY/RENT	BOUGHT	BUDGET	SPENT
Attire					
Shoes					
Accessories					
Alterations					

Wedding Attire

What are you going to wear to celebrate your wedding?

Your wedding day is a wonderful opportunity for you to dress snazzily, feel fabulous and embrace your inner Bridechilla and Groomchilla attitude. Choose attire that says 'you' rather than what you think you should wear.

Perhaps you have a clear picture of the look, feel, shape, color, and theme of your wedding day attire. Or, like many couples, you may have no idea what you are going to wear and can't picture yourself in any of the dresses or suits in wedding magazines. This is totally normal.

Shopping for your wedding day outfit doesn't have to be an event like something from a reality TV show. You don't have to cry or collapse on the ground in a sobbing mess when you've found 'the one'—you just have to feel freaking fabulous.

Before hitting the stores with anyone, why not take yourself out for a solo shopping trip? You don't have to try anything on, just take some time to peruse some stores and formulate a plan. Then you can make a list of where you may like to return with your designated helper(s).

Make sure that no matter the outfit you choose, you can still move, breathe, eat and feel comfortable in it. If a strapless dress isn't your style, ditch it. If you want to wear a jumpsuit, great. As long as what you choose makes you shine, then you are on the right track.

BRIDESMAIDS AND BRIDAL PARTY ATTIRE

When it comes to clothing the bridal party, get ready, it can be a hell of a ride.

This is your day and what you want is important, but you should also be aware when dressing your nearest and dearest friends for your wedding that they aren't Barbie and Ken dolls. They are individual humans with different body shapes, senses of style and their own free will. Not everyone is going to be happy and comfortable with what you may envisage them wearing. Which brings me to ask, why must we dress everyone in the same clothes? It's tradition of course.

I DARE YOU TO BREAK IT!

When looking at outfits and combinations for the bridal party, consider different body shapes and sizes. Who will be comfortable in what and is there a possibility of the attendants being able to re-wear their dress or suit in the future? Be open with communication, be a Bridechilla and think outside the outfit box.

NOTES

YOUR WEDDING ATTIRE

Name:

ITEM	IDEAS	WHERE TO BUY/RENT	BOUGHT	BUDGET	SPENT
Attire					
Shoes					
Accessories					
Alterations					

NOTES

Name:

ITEM	IDEAS	WHERE TO BUY/RENT	BOUGHT	BUDGET	SPENT
Attire					
Shoes					
Accessories					
Alterations					

NOTES

IMPERFECTION IS BEAUTY, MADNESS IS GENIUS, AND IT'S BETTER TO BE ABSOLUTELY RIDICULOUS THAN ABSOLUTELY BORING.

Marilyn Monroe

Hair & Makeup

Planning your hair and makeup look for your wedding day is fun but can also be a little daunting if you aren't a big wearer of makeup or if you don't spend much time with a hair straightener. A lot of the wedding media surrounding hair and makeup focuses on women who have long flowing hair and glowing skin—which is great for women who have access to all that hair and fabulous complexion but not as wonderful for the rest of us!

If makeup isn't part of your everyday routine, then you shouldn't feel pressured to suddenly embrace heavy makeup for your wedding day. You want to feel fabulous, and when it comes to hair and makeup a big part is finding a look that does just that. If you don't usually wear a lot of makeup, don't wear a lot on your wedding day. You aren't playing a character; it's not Halloween or a dress up party, it's your wedding.

A natural face, with beautiful dewy skin and light blush—can look very pretty. A lot of wedding makeup artists specialize in creating this look it helps even out your complexion without requiring heavy foundation and eye makeup.

If you are planning to work with a makeup artist and hairdresser on the day of your wedding, I strongly suggest that you arrange to have a trial. This gives you the opportunity to work together to achieve your desired look and get an idea of timings for the day. It is not offensive to makeup artists (and hairdressers) if you guide them with information about what you like and don't like. Go to your trial armed with images and examples of the looks you would like. If you have favorite colors or products, take them along too.

The more information the better!

THERE'S NO BETTER MAKEUP THAN CONFIDENCE.

Shakira

MAKEUP ARTIST:

Name: Notes:

Salon: Phone: Address:

Hours: Website: Email:

Trial Appointment Date & Time:

Trial Fee:

MAKEUP ARTIST:

Name: Notes:

Salon: Phone: Address:

Hours: Website: Email:

Trial Appointment Date & Time:

Trial Fee:

MAKEUP ARTIST:

Name: Notes:

Salon: Phone: Address:

Hours: Website: Email:

Trial Appointment Date & Time:

Trial Fee:

NOTES

HAIR STYLIST:

Name:

Notes:

Salon:

Phone:

Address:

Hours:

Website:

Email:

Trial Appointment Date & Time:

Trial Fee:

HAIR STYLIST:

Name:

Notes:

Salon:

Phone:

Address:

Hours:

Website:

Email:

Trial Appointment Date & Time:

Trial Fee:

HAIR STYLIST:

Name:

Notes:

Salon:

Phone:

Address:

Hours:

Website:

Email:

Trial Appointment Date & Time:

Trial Fee:

NOTES

NOTES

QUESTIONS TO ASK YOUR
HAIR & MAKEUP ARTIST

HAIR

Will you bring your own products (a blow dryer, curling iron and other necessities), or will I be responsible for supplying them?

Are you familiar with my particular skin or hair type?

How long will my hairstyle take?

How long before my wedding day should I have my hair trial?

What can I do to improve the condition of my hair?

What if I want to change my hair color?

How will I know if an up-do suits me?

Do you do hair extensions?

Should I arrive with just-washed hair on the wedding day? Should I use any leave-in products, deep conditioners? Should I straighten my hair before the trial run?

Should I bring my veil/accessories to the trial? What if I don't have them yet?

NOTES

NOTES

QUESTIONS TO ASK YOUR
HAIR & MAKEUP ARTIST

MAKEUP

Do you specialize in wedding makeup?

How long will makeup take on the day?

How long will you be onsite for on the day?

How long will the makeup trial take? Do I need to prepare for the trial and how do I prepare?

Will a fake tan affect my makeup?

What brands of makeup do you use?

Would you be open to using my own makeup?

Are false lashes or lash extensions included in your makeup package? Can you advise about top-ups for lipstick, powder etc?

I have sensitive skin and I am worried about wearing heavy makeup. Is this something you have dealt with before?

Are there any extra day-of charges I should know about?

If you are happy to travel to my location, do you have any specific space requirements for the trial and for the wedding day?

What will happen if you can't make it on my wedding day?

Do you want to see photos of hair and makeup looks I like?

What about photos of my wedding dress, decor, venue or other inspiration?

Do you have any other commitments on my wedding day?

Do you have a team of assistants or will you be the only stylist that day?

NOTES

LOVE IS TELLING SOMEONE THEIR HAIR EXTENSIONS ARE SHOWING.

Natasha Leggero

QUESTIONS TO ASK YOUR
HAIR & MAKEUP ARTIST

LOGISTICS

Can I see some examples of your work with former clients?

Can I contact them for references?

What does your price include?

If hair and makeup artists are working with the bridal party, what is their timing per client?

Do you charge per client or can I negotiate a package price?

Can I arrange to have a trial run before I pay the deposit?

Are you able to travel to our location?

Are there any extra charges—mileage, parking, travel, tolls?

I have an early wedding/large bridal party, will you be able to bring an assistant along on the wedding day if needed?

NOTES

The Guest List

"I don't want to leave people off the guest list, but I don't want to invite them either."

No matter how big or small your wedding celebrations will be, creating the guest list can be one of the most emotionally challenging exercises in the whole wedding planning adventure. There are many factors that go into creating a guest list: money, venue size, family expectations and what sort of vibe you want to create at your event.

Create a people-you-know brain dump.
Start big by creating your draft guest list. This is like a people-you-know brain dump. These people aren't all coming to your wedding, that much I can guarantee, but it is a good way to get it all down and see initially who stands out to you.

A couple of easy to answer questions that will help you make BIG decisions:

Are there names on the list that you don't recognize or people you hardly know?
DITCH THEM.

Ask, why are these people on your list? Do you like these people? No?
BYE!

Obligation Guests
What do you gain by having them attend the most intimate and personal moment potentially of your whole life? If I came along with a magic marker and removed them from the list how would you feel?

Create an A and B List
Unless money is no object or you have a large wedding venue, cutting the list is inevitable. Make an A and B List; with A the 'must invite' list and B the 'maybe but not

vital to invite' list. I've talked a lot about A and B lists on the Bridechilla Podcast, and I want to reiterate that putting people on the B list doesn't mean they are not as important to you or don't have value in your lives.

Perhaps your venue only holds 50 people, and you have 100 on your list, or perhaps your budget will only cover 30 people, and you have 400 people on your list! The guest list is as much circumstantial as it is emotive.

Ditch the obligation guests.
Obligation Guests are a **huge** challenge for many couples.

We ALL have them.

They're people who we think we should invite to the wedding, but if there was a way not to invite them, we would leave them off the list. They could be second cousins, co-workers or old college friends. Most of us feel obliged to invite them because we're nice. We don't want to let them down, or make people feel bad that they weren't invited.

Here are some questions I would like you to consider when creating your guest list:
Would you shout these people a $200 dinner any other day?
Would you regret not sharing this important day in your lives with this person?
Will seeing these people on your wedding day make you feel joy?

Bridechillas and Groomchillas don't fake smile on their wedding day.
Your wedding should be about your future, not just your past. So it's important to invite people who you want in your future, not people you feel obliged to invite to save face or momentary feelings of awkwardness.

THE GUEST LIST

NAME	INVITED	ATTENDING

THE GUEST LIST

NAME	INVITED	ATTENDING

THE GUEST LIST

NAME	INVITED	ATTENDING

THE GUEST LIST

NAME	INVITED	ATTENDING

MARRIAGE HAS NO GUARANTEES. IF THAT'S WHAT YOU'RE LOOKING FOR, GO LIVE WITH A CAR BATTERY.

Erma Bombeck

Seating Plans...
Who Sits Where?

Setting up a wedding seating chart is a bit like playing Tetris with people.

Some couples prefer a 'sit where you please approach', while others meticulously plan their seating placements around themes such as family politics, relationship status, second cousins, and vegans.

Finalizing your seating plans will most likely happen after you receive your RSVPs. Look at your venue space and speak with your venue coordinator about the table options and how they have set the room up before. This will give you an opportunity to envisage the space and how you would like your guests to be placed.

Your venue may provide tables and linen that fit the space, or you may have to hire them. Consider the shape of tables and the different atmospheres seating plans can create.

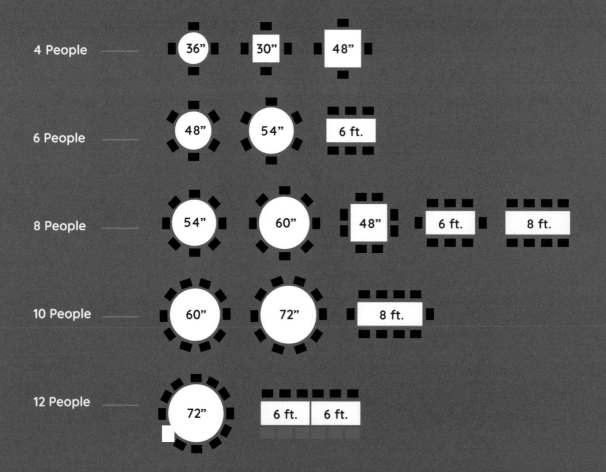

4 People — 36" 30" 48"

6 People — 48" 54" 6 ft.

8 People — 54" 60" 48" 6 ft. 8 ft.

10 People — 60" 72" 8 ft.

12 People — 72" 6 ft. 6 ft.

THE SEATING PLAN

Table number and name:

_____   _____
_____   _____
_____   _____
_____   _____
_____   _____
_____   _____
_____   _____

Table number and name:

_____   _____
_____   _____
_____   _____
_____   _____
_____   _____
_____   _____
_____   _____

Table number and name:

_____   _____
_____   _____
_____   _____
_____   _____
_____   _____
_____   _____

THE SEATING PLAN

Table number and name:

_____   _____
_____   _____
_____   _____
_____   _____
_____   _____
_____   _____
_____   _____

Table number and name:

_____   _____
_____   _____
_____   _____
_____   _____
_____   _____
_____   _____
_____   _____

Table number and name:

_____   _____
_____   _____
_____   _____
_____   _____
_____   _____
_____   _____
_____   _____

THE SEATING PLAN

Table number and name:

_____   _____
_____   _____
_____   _____
_____   _____
_____   _____
_____   _____
_____   _____

Table number and name:

_____   _____
_____   _____
_____   _____
_____   _____
_____   _____
_____   _____
_____   _____

Table number and name:

_____   _____
_____   _____
_____   _____
_____   _____
_____   _____
_____   _____

THERE'S NO SUCH THING AS FUN FOR THE WHOLE FAMILY.

Jerry Seinfeld

THE SEATING PLAN

Table number and name:

_____   _____
_____   _____
_____   _____
_____   _____
_____   _____
_____   _____
_____   _____

Table number and name:

_____   _____
_____   _____
_____   _____
_____   _____
_____   _____
_____   _____
_____   _____

Table number and name:

_____   _____
_____   _____
_____   _____
_____   _____
_____   _____
_____   _____
_____   _____

FLOWERS

	FLOWER AND DESIGN IDEAS	QUANTITY	ESTIMATED COST	TOTAL
BOUQUET				
CORSAGES				
BOUTONNIERES				
BRIDESMAIDS' BOUQUETS				
CEREMONY FLOWERS				
RECEPTION FLOWERS				
OTHER				
OTHER				

Flowers

Flowers are marvelous, especially at weddings, but the cost of flowers can quickly turn your floral centerpiece dreams into nightmares.

When selecting wedding flowers (if you want flowers at all) it's a smart idea to choose blooms that are in season, as they will be cheaper and, most importantly, readily available. You would be surprised how many flowers are flown in from all over the world, which can be very costly. Speak with your florist about what is in season and work backwards from there.

You don't need a massive floral centerpiece to make the table gorgeous. In fact, you don't need flowers on the table at all.

If you are keen on having some 'living' centerpiece but can't afford a full floral arrangement, then visit your local garden center or nursery and buy several trays of annuals or perennials that match your color scheme. You could also choose herbs, like oregano, basil and tarragon, which will give any setting an organic feel. Plus I guarantee they will be snapped up by the guests to take home at the end of the day.

Flowers are beautiful, so why not let someone else enjoy the beauty of your wedding flowers when you are off whooping it up on honeymoon? I am talking about the idea that you can recycle your flowers by donating them to hospices, hospitals and old folks' homes. In fact, there are many charities and organizations that will come to your venue and collect them after the wedding. You'll never have to do anything out of your schedule, and often a lot of hotels and event companies will be involved with the charity as well.

Ask your wedding planner or venue if they are connected with one of these charities or organizations, and if they aren't, ask why not and what the hell they do with the flowers from all the functions they hold?!

Can you imagine someone's nanna being able to have fresh flowers in her room, or terminally ill people in a hospice having lovely flowers? How nice is it to think that you can pass on these beautiful floral arrangements that you've had at your wedding and know that they will bring a bit of joy into other people's lives. That is the ultimate Bridechilla & Groomchilla move.

NOTES

FLORISTS

Vendor:

Company: _____

Contact name: _____

Number: _____

Email: _____

Address: _____

Price: _____

Package: _____

_____

Notes: _____

PAYMENT DETAILS   Date 1 _____ ☐ Paid   Date 2 _____ ☐ Paid

Vendor:

Company: _____

Contact name: _____

Number: _____

Email: _____

Address: _____

Price: _____

Package: _____

_____

Notes: _____

PAYMENT DETAILS   Date 1 _____ ☐ Paid   Date 2 _____ ☐ Paid

Vendor:

Company: _____

Contact name: _____

Number: _____

Email: _____

Address: _____

Price: _____

Package: _____

_____

Notes: _____

PAYMENT DETAILS   Date 1 _____ ☐ Paid   Date 2 _____ ☐ Paid

QUESTIONS FOR FLORISTS

Can we contact past clients for references?

Can we see a portfolio of photographs from previous weddings you have worked on?

Is our budget feasible?

Is there a specific style you prefer?

Are you available on our chosen wedding date?

How do you charge—flat fee or per item? Is there a delivery charge?

Do you have liability insurance?

What is the refund/cancellation process?

When is payment due?

How long have you been doing weddings?

Are all the flower options customized or are there set packages?

Will you be working on any other weddings on our selected date?

Can you advise on linen, chairs and table settings?

Do you work directly with wedding planners or coordinators?

What flowers are in season during our wedding month?

What flowers do you think would work with our budget?

Is there a delivery or on-site set up fee?

Would you be willing to make a mock-up bouquet or other arrangements?

NOTES

NOTES

NOTES

QUESTIONS FOR FLORISTS

Have you worked at our venue before? If not, are you available for a consultation and will you charge for it?

Do you provide any other accessories, like vases and candles? If you do, how much are they and are they included in the price?

How much time will it take to set the flowers up at the venue?

What time will the flowers (and florist) be arriving?

Where will your flowers be delivered and who will be setting them up?

How much would it cost to move the flowers from the ceremony to the reception venue?

If the flowers we choose aren't available on the day, who picks the substitute?

Will you collect any rental items, vases, etc., after the wedding?

What are the breakage and refund policies?

If we are collecting the flowers before our wedding, is there anything special we need to do to keep them fresh and alive?

Are you happy to work with our cake maker if we want to decorate the cake with flowers?

How far in advance should I order the flowers?

Do you have any references from recent customers?

When should I pay the full sum?

Should I pay in cash or with a check?

NOTES

Decor, Lighting & DIY

To DIY or not to DIY, that is the question

Before committing to a DIY project to save money, consider the time and effort that is going to go into this project and the cost of the tools to make it happen. I am the first to admit that I get quickly carried away with crafty missions that I think are going to save me both time and money.

I'm pretty handy but even still, 95% of my projects come in over budget, and I am left with tools that live in the bottom drawer of the kitchen just begging to be used. Is it worth spending every night for three weeks cutting and gluing and getting angry at staples to save $50?

Your time is valuable, particularly in the months leading up to your wedding. Wouldn't you rather relax and have a wine instead of having a breakdown over folding paper? I'm all up for DIY, just know what you are in for before buying all the gear.

Before you DIY

- Price out the project. Is DIY the cheaper option?
- What other tools and materials do you need to buy? Can you re-use materials and tools?

Value your time

Take on projects you will enjoy and not loathe within three minutes. If you want the DIY look but aren't keen on DIY, hire a creative person from Fiverr or Upwork or support an artist/creative person and buy items from Etsy.

Lighting is magic

An often undervalued but affordable addition to your decor plan is lighting. I'm not just talking about disco balls, lasers, and spotlights (although all have their place at a party amirite?!).

Simple uplighting and colorful washes can make a big difference to the mood of a venue. If there is a plain wall that you would like to sass up, see what you can do to it with lights.

Consider planning subtle lighting changes as your event progresses. Research what lighting other events at your venue have used (use Instagram) and ask if you can visit the venue in the evening to see what it looks like in the dark. Candles are great for ambiance but be sure to check with your venue and find out if they are permitted. If they are a no-go, you can use realistic battery operated candles instead.

NOTES

NOTES

WEDDING DECOR

Ceremony

AISLE & CHAIRS:

ALTAR:

Reception

CENTER PIECES:

TABLES & CHAIRS:

CAKE TABLE:

GUEST BOOK TABLE/GIFT TABLE

OTHER:

NOTES

DECOR CONTACTS

Vendor:

Company:

Contact name:

Number:

Email:

Address:

Price:

Package:

Notes:

PAYMENT DETAILS   Date 1 _____ ☐ Paid   Date 2 _____ ☐ Paid

Vendor:

Company:

Contact name:

Number:

Email:

Address:

Price:

Package:

Notes:

PAYMENT DETAILS   Date 1 _____ ☐ Paid   Date 2 _____ ☐ Paid

Vendor:

Company:

Contact name:

Number:

Email:

Address:

Price:

Package:

Notes:

PAYMENT DETAILS   Date 1 _____ ☐ Paid   Date 2 _____ ☐ Paid

Stationery & Invitations

••••

Your wedding invitations and stationery (including Save The Date cards) set the stage for your whole event.

They are your guests' first impression of your wedding and they set up their expectations of the event.

Ultimately the purpose of a wedding invitation is to convey information:

Who is invited
What they are invited to
When they are required to be there
What else they need to do and bring

The look of the invitation is how you convey the tone and overall vibe of your wedding. It is important that the content of the invitation is easy to interpret and understand, and includes necessary information such as addresses. If the destination is hard to find, directions to the wedding or reception will also be appreciated by your guests.

The look of your wedding stationery should connect with your wedding theme or colors or at least have some synergy with the sort of party that you intend to plan.

Delegating the design of your wedding stationery to an expert is easy. There are many talented independent designers who will do custom designs. Hiring a graphic designer from websites such as 99designs.com, upwork.com, fiverr.com and Etsy to design your wedding stationery can be a wise move, particularly if you are time poor or perhaps not that confident with your Photoshop skills.

It's exciting to work with a designer who gets what you want and whose professional eye and creativity can add to your ideas and bring them to life. Using a professional also comes in handy when you are ready to print your designs—they will be able to help you with bleed and color settings that all professional printers, even the cheaper online ones, require.

STATIONERY ITEMS

ITEM	QUANTITY	CONSTRUCTION	ORDERED	MADE	MAIL BY
Save the date		DIY / Purchase			
Invitation		DIY / Purchase			
Place card		DIY / Purchase			
Table number		DIY / Purchase			
Seating plan		DIY / Purchase			
Menu		DIY / Purchase			
Ceremony program		DIY / Purchase			

NOTES

STATIONERS

Vendor:

Company:

Contact name:

Number:

Email:

Address:

Price:

Package:

Notes:

PAYMENT DETAILS	Date 1	Paid	Date 2	Paid

Vendor:

Company:

Contact name:

Number:

Email:

Address:

Price:

Package:

Notes:

PAYMENT DETAILS	Date 1	Paid	Date 2	Paid

Vendor:

Company:

Contact name:

Number:

Email:

Address:

Price:

Package:

Notes:

PAYMENT DETAILS	Date 1	Paid	Date 2	Paid

QUESTIONS TO ASK YOUR STATIONERY DESIGNER & PRINTER

What types of printing and design do you offer and which do you specialize in?

What would you recommend for our budget and style?

Is your printing done in-house or do you outsource it?

Do you offer custom invitations as well as templated styles?

Is there a fee if we order a sample of either an existing invitation style or a custom design?

If we choose a custom design, what are our options for color, paper type, ink and fonts?

What is the word limit for the text?

Can we order our table numbers, place cards, ceremony programs, menus, etc. from you?

Do you offer a package or a discounted price if we order everything at the same time?

Are there any new styles, trends or color combinations we should consider?

What kinds of handmade or artisanal paper do you offer?

Do you offer recycled paper or any other eco-friendly materials?

If the invitation involves multiple pieces, can you assemble them? If so, is there an additional fee?

NOTES

NOTES

NOTES

QUESTIONS TO ASK YOUR STATIONERY DESIGNER & PRINTER

Based on the paper we select and the number of pieces involved, what would it cost to mail our wedding invitations?

How long will it take to have the completed invitations delivered?

Do you have rush-order available and are there extra fees?

What shipping methods are available, and what are their respective costs?

Do you offer an invitation addressing service? If so, what is the charge for this?

When is payment due?

Will we have an opportunity to sign off on our invitation proof before you send our order to print?

If there are printing errors will our invitations be corrected and reprinted at no additional cost?

What is your refund policy if we need to cancel our order?

When can we expect to receive our contract from you?

Can you provide us with the contact information of 3-4 recent customers who we can call or email for references?

NOTES

Music & Entertainment

You've found the venue, you've thought about what to eat and drink, now it's time to consider the party and the extra elements that you can add to make the event truly memorable.

What sort of atmosphere do you want your wedding day to have?

Will the reception be filled with dancing and laughter? Hopefully!

If so, is there somewhere for this frivolity to occur—room for a dance floor? Is there a place where senior guests can sit around and discuss all the other guests?

When it comes to creating a party atmosphere, your guests will contribute to the ambiance. But having a live band or a DJ to get people in the dancing mood can make a difference—compared to just plugging your iPod into house speakers and getting drunk Uncle Joe to yell at everyone "Get up and DANCE!"

Part of the magic of wedding planning, no matter the budget, is giving yourself permission to inject your personality and creativity into your music and entertainment design, while also finding the sweet spot for your guests to dance, mingle and if you so choose, rock the hell out!

Creating atmosphere isn't just about decoration and visual aesthetics, it's also about setting a tone with lighting and music.

Think about your guests and your expectations for your party.

What sort of music will get them up out of their seats and moving?
Are they old or young?
Will they dance at all?
What mood do you want to create? If you have decided on a renaissance recreation wedding, a local punk band might not be that appropriate.
Do you want live music, or would an iPod or Spotify playlist suffice?

TRUST ME,
YOU CAN DANCE

Vodka

NOTES

ENTERTAINMENT CONTACTS

Vendor:

Company: Price:

Contact name: Package:

Number:

Email:

Address: Notes:

PAYMENT DETAILS   Date 1   Paid   Date 2   Paid

Vendor:

Company: Price:

Contact name: Package:

Number:

Email:

Address: Notes:

PAYMENT DETAILS   Date 1   Paid   Date 2   Paid

Vendor:

Company: Price:

Contact name: Package:

Number:

Email:

Address: Notes:

PAYMENT DETAILS   Date 1   Paid   Date 2   Paid

THE MUSIC

CEREMONY

Prelude

Entrance

Recession

Postlude

Other

RECEPTION

Background music

First dance

Special songs

Other

DO NOT PLAY LIST

You're the One That I Want - Grease

FAVORITE SONGS

QUESTIONS TO ASK YOUR WEDDING DJ OR BAND

Is our wedding date available?

How long have you been in business?

How long have you been performing?

How many hours are included in the package?

Do you perform at more than one event in a day?

Have you performed at our venue before?

What are your power and amplification requirements?

Do you provide microphones and sound for the ceremony?

What equipment do you provide and what equipment do we need to provide ourselves?

Can you play the songs that are important to us, such as a traditional Jewish hora tune or our favorite B-side?

How extensive is your music library or song list?

What genres can you cover?

Are you happy to add songs that we request beforehand?

How do you keep your music collection up to date?

How do you handle song requests?

NOTES

QUESTIONS TO ASK YOUR WEDDING DJ OR BAND

How many musicians are in the band, and available?

How many vocalists?

Are there different options for how many musicians/instruments we can hire?

Can you act as the master of ceremonies (MC)?

Do you plan to use lighting or any other special effects?

What are your set up timings and requirements?

Do you take any breaks?

What music will be provided during the breaks?

How many band members will perform that day?

What do you typically wear when you DJ/perform?

What's your sick-day policy?

Do you have liability insurance?

What's your backup plan if there's an equipment malfunction?

What's your cancellation policy?

How do you get people up and dancing if they are a bit shy or hesitant?

NOTES

BE YOURSELF; EVERYONE ELSE IS ALREADY TAKEN.

Oscar Wilde

Photography & Videography

Photography is important. Very important. After your wedding is over, the one thing (besides memories) that you can always look at, to remember and relive moments from your celebration, are your wedding photographs. Images and video will transport you back to the people and special moments that made your celebration. Good photography also captures the feelings and vibes from the day.

When you imagine your wedding photographs, what springs to mind? Do you envisage having a photographer with you from early in the day, capturing the pre-wedding preparation? Or are you more interested in having someone there for longer to photograph the celebration, dancing, and frivolities?

This is not a trick question, you can have both!

Photos tell the story of your day. They capture moments that will trigger memories of people and details of an experience that often passes far too quickly. Finding the right person, with the right skills, to ensure that your memories live on can be challenging, particularly when you may not have decided what style of photography you are after.

As with canvassing for vendors and venues, having a budget in mind will make your search a lot easier. If you have a photographer who doesn't shoot for under $5,000 and your total wedding budget is $7,000, this perhaps isn't going to work for you. Expand your horizons and move on.

When you do find a photographer whose style you like, explore their portfolio and read testimonials. What are your initial impressions?

Think about the level of service that you require. A wedding photographer who provides no pre-wedding planning service and just turns up on the day, shoots and hands over a disk of unedited images provides a very different service to a wedding photographer who individually edits each image. Each scenario will bring a different cost.

Consider wisely.

NOTES

PHOTOGRAPHERS

Vendor:

Company: _____

Contact name: _____

Number: _____

Email: _____

Address: _____

Price: _____

Package: _____

_____

Notes: _____

PAYMENT DETAILS   Date 1 _____ ☐ Paid   Date 2 _____ ☐ Paid

Vendor:

Company: _____

Contact name: _____

Number: _____

Email: _____

Address: _____

Price: _____

Package: _____

_____

Notes: _____

PAYMENT DETAILS   Date 1 _____ ☐ Paid   Date 2 _____ ☐ Paid

Vendor:

Company: _____

Contact name: _____

Number: _____

Email: _____

Address: _____

Price: _____

Package: _____

_____

Notes: _____

PAYMENT DETAILS   Date 1 _____ ☐ Paid   Date 2 _____ ☐ Paid

NOTES

VIDEOGRAPHERS

Vendor:

Company: _____

Contact name: _____

Number: _____

Email: _____

Address: _____

Price: _____

Package: _____

_____

Notes: _____

PAYMENT DETAILS	Date 1 _____	☐ Paid	Date 2 _____	☐ Paid

Vendor:

Company: _____

Contact name: _____

Number: _____

Email: _____

Address: _____

Price: _____

Package: _____

_____

Notes: _____

PAYMENT DETAILS	Date 1 _____	☐ Paid	Date 2 _____	☐ Paid

Vendor:

Company: _____

Contact name: _____

Number: _____

Email: _____

Address: _____

Price: _____

Package: _____

_____

Notes: _____

PAYMENT DETAILS	Date 1 _____	☐ Paid	Date 2 _____	☐ Paid

QUESTIONS TO ASK YOUR PHOTOGRAPHER

How far in advance do we need to book?

Are you available on our wedding date?

Have you ever shot at our wedding venue?

Do you offer different packages?

Have you had broad experience working with a variety of people?

How long have you been working as a professional photographer?

How would you describe your photography style?

How flexible is your style?

Do you have a portfolio we can review?

Are all of the images yours, and is the work recent?

Can you share some recent testimonials?

What type of equipment do you use?

Are you shooting in digital or film format or both?

Can we give you a list of specific shots we would like?

If our wedding site is out of your area, do you charge a travel fee and what does that cover?

Will you be photographing other events on the same day as our wedding?

If our event lasts longer than expected, will you stay? Is there an additional charge?

How much would it cost for an additional hour?

NOTES

NOTES

QUESTIONS TO ASK YOUR PHOTOGRAPHER

Do you work with a second shooter?

Who owns the copyright of the photographs?

How many photos will we receive from our wedding?

What is the delivery time for the final images?

What is your social media policy?

What is your refund/cancellation policy?

What happens if you are ill, or there is an emergency?

Do you have liability insurance?

Can we customize a package based on our needs?

Do you include engagement photos in your packages?

What type of album designs do you offer?

Do you provide any assistance in creating an album?

Do you provide retouching, color adjustment or other corrective services?

How long after the wedding will we get the proofs?

Will the images be viewable online?

What is the ordering process?

How long after we order our photos/album will we get them?

Will you give us the negatives or the digital images, and is there a fee for that?

NOTES

NOTES

NOTES

QUESTIONS TO ASK YOUR VIDEOGRAPHER

How will you coordinate the filming of our wedding with the photographer?
Are you available on our wedding date?
What types of packages do you offer?
How many weddings have you filmed?
What parts of the wedding day do you capture?
Is the videographer we are meeting the same person who will be filming on our wedding day?
How many videographers will be filming at our wedding?
How do you film the ceremony and speeches?
How would you describe your production style (documentary, cinematic, vintage)?
Is your shooting approach direct or more journalistic?
How do you record audio—camera mounted microphones or lapels?
Does the final video use dialogue from the wedding day or is it more of a music video?
Do you use additional lights during the reception?

NOTES

NOTES

QUESTIONS TO ASK YOUR VIDEOGRAPHER

Do you have backup equipment in case of equipment failure?

How is footage recorded?

How do you deliver the final product?

Can we see a finished sample?

How long will it take you to edit our video?

Can we select the music for the wedding video?

How do you back up your footage?

How long do you keep the footage?

How long will the final product be?

How many copies of the final film will we receive?

Are changes available once we see a first edit?

What music will you be using in our wedding video?

What is your social media policy?

NOTES

BITCHES GET STUFF DONE.

Tina Fey

Wedding Transport

If your ceremony and reception are at the same venue, pat yourself on the back, you get ten gold stars for convenience! If your ceremony and reception venues are in different places, however, then you will need a plan for how you and your guests will get from one place to the other.

Providing guest transportation isn't a deal breaker. In fact, most guests wouldn't expect transport to be included (unless you are away from civilization). But be conscious of guests driving after drinking; if you can offer other options to help them get home, do.

Use Uber and Lyft As Wedding Cars
The shared economy is a marvelous thing. Uber and Lyft have jumped on board the wedding train (apologies for the mixed metaphors) and are offering a number of options for you and your guests if you are getting married where their services are available.

Before you start the, "Hey Aleisha, I don't want to be picked up by some Bluetooth-wearing guy who plays talkback radio too loudly and drives his Prius like it's a getaway car to my wedding,"—just relax. Lyft Lux and Uber Lux both offer snazzy cars that are specifically for transporting people to events like weddings and business meetings.

Although you can't "book" a car in advance, if you order with enough lead time—which will be easier if you are getting married in a place like a city or large metro area—the car will get you there just fine.

Discount Codes
For transporting your guests, both Uber and Lyft have special "Events" pages where you can create personalized discount codes for your guests to use. You can also add credit to the event page to either pay for their rides or give your guests a discount.*

Guests that want to participate simply download the Uber or Lyft app, then they can use your personalized promo code to receive a discount. For new ride share app users, another option is to give them your personal referral code (which you can create within both apps). They receive a discount, and you receive credit after they ride. Winner!

*Discounts vary from location to location.

NOTES

WEDDING TRANSPORT CONTACTS

Vendor:

Company:

Contact name:

Number:

Email:

Address:

Price:

Package:

Notes:

PAYMENT DETAILS   Date 1 _____ ☐ Paid   Date 2 _____ ☐ Paid

Vendor:

Company:

Contact name:

Number:

Email:

Address:

Price:

Package:

Notes:

PAYMENT DETAILS   Date 1 _____ ☐ Paid   Date 2 _____ ☐ Paid

Vendor:

Company:

Contact name:

Number:

Email:

Address:

Price:

Package:

Notes:

PAYMENT DETAILS   Date 1 _____ ☐ Paid   Date 2 _____ ☐ Paid

Vows & The Ceremony

Whether you are choosing to have a civil or religious ceremony, injecting a little bit of "you" into the vows is a wonderful way to express how you feel about each other. Considering all the logistics of wedding planning, sometimes the wedding ceremony itself becomes an afterthought. Don't let this happen. This is the main event!

Personalization

Often celebrants and ministers will help you write and structure your vows and will work with you to personalize the ceremony. Some religions insist that you use the canonical wording, but others may allow you to also include individulized segments. Hopefully the officiant will ask you to share details about your relationship and may even invite you to write your own vows to help shape the ceremony.

Wedding vows can be short and sweet or long and personal. Some vows make guests laugh, while others invoke happy tears. Don't miss this moment to make your vows shine.

If the prospect of writing vows or taking the ceremony beyond 'to have and to hold' overwhelms you, here are some very simple questions that you can both answer to begin the process of tailoring your vows and making them truly about you. It doesn't have to be smooshy or overly sentimental if that isn't your style, but adding your story to the ceremony will make the process even more meaningful.

Don't be afraid to add humor. Be authentic and consider the tone of your wedding and how you can make your ceremony truly reflect your relationship.

BEFORE YOU
MARRY A PERSON
YOU SHOULD FIRST
MAKE THEM USE A
COMPUTER WITH
SLOW INTERNET
TO SEE WHO THEY
REALLY ARE.

Will Ferrell

QUESTIONS TO HELP SHAPE YOUR VOWS

Name:

What is your most favorite memory of your partner?

When did you realize that you wanted to marry your partner?

Are there any readings that you would like to include in the ceremony?

What commitments would you like to make to your partner?

What are three things that make your relationship work?

What does your partner bring to your union?

Describe your partner in three words?

QUESTIONS TO HELP SHAPE YOUR VOWS

What are some quotes or sayings that have been meaningful to your relationship?

What will change about your relationship once you are married?

What will stay the same?

What would you want everyone to know about your partner and why you love them?

How did your life change when you met your partner?

What are three funny things that your partner does that irk you?

What are your goals for the future?

What do you look forward to the most when you see your partner?

QUESTIONS TO HELP SHAPE YOUR VOWS

Name:

What is your most favorite memory of your partner?

When did you realize that you wanted to marry your partner?

Are there any readings that you would like to include in the ceremony?

What commitments would you like to make to your partner?

What are three things that make your relationship work?

What does your partner bring to your union?

Describe your partner in three words?

QUESTIONS TO HELP SHAPE YOUR VOWS

What are some quotes or sayings that have been meaningful to your relationship?

What will change about your relationship once you are married?

What will stay the same?

What would you want everyone to know about your partner and why you love them?

How did your life change when you met your partner?

What are three funny things that your partner does that irk you?

What are your goals for the future?

What do you look forward to the most when you see your partner?

NOTES

OFFICIANT CONTACTS

Name:

Company:

Contact name:

Number:

Email:

Address:

Price:

Package:

Notes:

PAYMENT DETAILS   Date 1   Paid   Date 2   Paid

Name:

Company:

Contact name:

Number:

Email:

Address:

Price:

Package:

Notes:

PAYMENT DETAILS   Date 1   Paid   Date 2   Paid

Name:

Company:

Contact name:

Number:

Email:

Address:

Price:

Package:

Notes:

PAYMENT DETAILS   Date 1   Paid   Date 2   Paid

QUESTIONS TO ASK YOUR OFFICIANT

Are you available on our wedding date?

Can you travel to our wedding site?

What are your fees?

What do the fees include?

Do you have any sample wording/ceremonies/readings to share with us?

What is your biggest challenge when officiating a wedding?

Can we specify ceremony details such as music, readings, and vows?

Can we include religious touches if desired?

Do you turn in the marriage license for us or will we have to do it?

Can you legally perform the ceremony in our city/state/county?

Can you customize the ceremony to include rituals, special readings, etc.?

NOTES

QUESTIONS TO ASK YOUR OFFICIANT

What is your religious affiliation (or lack thereof)?

How many weddings have you performed?

Are you LGBTQ+ friendly?

Will you perform the rehearsal or does it cost extra?

Does it cost extra to personalize the ceremony?

Do you have a video we can watch of you at a recent ceremony?

How long do your ceremonies usually last?

How many pre-wedding sessions will we have with you?

Will you help us obtain our marriage license?

What do you enjoy about celebrating weddings?

Do you have any references from couples you have officiated for?

NOTES

RELIGIOUS OFFICIANT

Are you willing to marry us at a nonreligious site?
Will you perform an interfaith ceremony?

THINGS TO CONSIDER

Does the officiant make you comfortable?
Does he or she seem genuinely interested in you as a couple?

Be sure you like and respect your officiant and that the feeling is mutual.

NOTES

REAL LOVE AMOUNTS TO WITHHOLDING THE TRUTH, EVEN WHEN YOU'RE OFFERED THE PERFECT OPPORTUNITY TO HURT SOMEONE'S FEELINGS.

David Sedaris

OBVIOUSLY, IF
I WAS SERIOUS
ABOUT HAVING A
RELATIONSHIP WITH
SOMEONE LONG-
TERM, THE LAST
PEOPLE I WOULD
INTRODUCE HIM
TO WOULD BE
MY FAMILY.

Chelsea Handler

WEDDING ACCOMMODATION

Name: **Address:**

RESERVATION DETAILS:

_____

Check in time: Check out time:

Name: **Address:**

RESERVATION DETAILS:

_____

Check in time: Check out time:

Name: **Address:**

RESERVATION DETAILS:

_____

Check in time: Check out time:

Name: **Address:**

RESERVATION DETAILS:

_____

Check in time: Check out time:

Name: **Address:**

RESERVATION DETAILS:

_____

Check in time: Check out time:

TEN HONEYMOON IDEAS

1.
2.
3.
4.
5.
6.
7.
8.
9.
10.

HONEYMOON AND TRAVEL

Destination:

GOING THERE

Departure time: from

Arrival time: at

Flight details:

Date: **to**

COMING BACK

Departure time: from

Arrival time: at

Flight details:

ACCOMMODATION

Name: **Address:**

RESERVATION DETAILS:

Check in time: Check out time:

TRANSPORT ONCE THERE

Car hire   **Public transport:**

DETAILS:

NOTES

Wedding Day Emergency Kit

IMPORTANT THINGS

Wedding dress ☐
Suit, tie, cufflinks ☐
Veil or headpiece ☐
Underwear & hosiery ☐
Shoes ☐
Something old, new, borrowed and blue ☐
Jewelry ☐
Contact list and time line for the day ☐
Copies of vendor and bridal party contacts ☐
Marriage license ☐
Wedding bands ☐
Copy of your wedding toast ☐
Envelopes with tips for vendors ☐

THE "OH SHIT" KIT*

Double-stick tape ☐
Earring backs ☐
Snacks (cake!) ☐
Hairspray, brush & comb ☐
Gel or mousse ☐
Deodorant ☐
Band-aids (clear) ☐
Safety pins, bobby pins and elastic bands ☐
Hair dryer ☐
Pain reliever ☐
Tissues and baby wipes ☐
Clear nail varnish ☐
Lipstick and lip liner ☐
Tampons and pads ☐
Toothbrush, toothpaste and floss ☐
Makeup ☐
Sewing kit (with white and ivory thread, extra buttons) ☐

*Or save time and go to **bridechillastore.com** to grab our ready-made 'Oh Sh*it kit'. BAM.

Sample Wedding Day Time Line

One of the biggest keys to being a calm couple is being clear about the logistics of your wedding day—basically everything you have been working on in this field guide. Your day doesn't have to be run like a military operation, but it is important that vendors know what time to arrive and where to set up. Communicate with your venue and vendors about the timing for the day.

This is where having a wedding planner or coordinator really pays for itself. A professional organizer, someone who knows all the ins and outs of the logistical aspects and timing of a wedding day, can make things much easier for you and will ensure that you aren't having to think about whether the bartender has turned up or if the cake has been delivered.

If you are organizing your own time line, start to add information as you receive it, so you can coordinate timing. If you know that your venue requires you and your guests to depart at 10pm, work backwards from there. Make sure that your venue and key vendors have a copy of your time line and share it with a few trusted people who can oversee the day.

Give yourself plenty of time.

Speak with vendors about their expectations for timing. For example, photographers may wish for you to allocate a specific amount of time for pictures after the ceremony. They will also take note of specific lighting timings, such as sunset. Hair and makeup artists will also be able to give you an indicator of time required. If you are DIYing any parts of the day, be sure to allocate extra contingency time so you aren't rushed or panicked if things are slower than initially expected.

SAMPLE RUNDOWN

9:00 AM	Hair & makeup begins for bridesmaids, followed by bride.
9:00 AM	Wedding set up begins / rental company begins set up at reception location
11:00 AM	Groom and groomsmen meet to begin preparing
12:00 PM	Lunch hour
1:00 PM	Flowers delivered to bridal suite, groom suite, and ceremony and reception site
2:00 PM	Getting ready photos of bride and bridesmaids (bridal suite) and groom and groomsmen (groom suite)
3:00 PM	First look photos (if applicable)
3:30 PM	Ceremony music starts. Guests begin to arrive.
4:00 PM	Wedding party all on location
4:30 PM	Ceremony
5:30 PM	Cocktail hour / family and wedding party photos
6:30 PM	Couple entrance and wedding party
6:45 PM	Dinner
7:30 PM	Toasts
8:00 PM	Dancing kicks off
8:30 PM	Cake cutting
9:00 PM	Bouquet toss
9:45 PM	Last dance
10:00 PM	After party

IMPORTANT CONTACTS

Name:

Company:

Number:

Email:

Address:

Details:

Package:

Notes:

Name:

Company:

Number:

Email:

Address:

Details:

Package:

Notes:

Name:

Company:

Number:

Email:

Address:

Details:

Package:

Notes:

Name:

Company:

Number:

Email:

Address:

Details:

Package:

Notes:

IMPORTANT CONTACTS

Name:

Company: _____

Number: _____

Email: _____

Address: _____

_____

_____

Details: _____

Package: _____

Notes: _____

_____

_____

Name:

Company: _____

Number: _____

Email: _____

Address: _____

_____

_____

Details: _____

Package: _____

Notes: _____

_____

_____

Name:

Company: _____

Number: _____

Email: _____

Address: _____

_____

_____

Details: _____

Package: _____

Notes: _____

_____

_____

Name:

Company: _____

Number: _____

Email: _____

Address: _____

Details: _____

Package: _____

Notes: _____

IMPORTANT CONTACTS

Name:

Company:

Number:

Email:

Address:

Details:

Package:

Notes:

Name:

Company:

Number:

Email:

Address:

Details:

Package:

Notes:

Name:

Company:

Number:

Email:

Address:

Details:

Package:

Notes:

Name:

Company:

Number:

Email:

Address:

Details:

Package:

Notes:

IMPORTANT CONTACTS

Name:

Company:

Number:

Email:

Address:

Details:

Package:

Notes:

Name:

Company:

Number:

Email:

Address:

Details:

Package:

Notes:

Name:

Company:

Number:

Email:

Address:

Details:

Package:

Notes:

Name:

Company:

Number:

Email:

Address:

Details:

Package:

Notes:

WEDDING DAY TIME LINE

TIME	EVENT
:	
:	
:	
:	
:	
:	
:	
:	
:	
:	
:	
:	
:	
:	
:	
:	
:	
:	
:	
:	
:	
:	
:	
:	
:	
:	
:	
:	
:	

WEDDING DAY TIME LINE

TIME	EVENT
:	
:	
:	
:	
:	
:	
:	
:	
:	
:	
:	
:	
:	
:	
:	
:	
:	
:	
:	
:	
:	
:	
:	
:	
:	
:	
:	
:	

WEDDING DAY TIME LINE

TIME	EVENT
:	
:	
:	
:	
:	
:	
:	
:	
:	
:	
:	
:	
:	
:	
:	
:	
:	
:	
:	
:	
:	
:	
:	
:	
:	
:	

WEDDING DAY TIME LINE

TIME	EVENT
:	
:	
:	
:	
:	
:	
:	
:	
:	
:	
:	
:	
:	
:	
:	
:	
:	
:	
:	
:	
:	
:	
:	
:	
:	
:	
:	

TO BUY

Name:

ITEM	IDEAS	WHERE TO BUY/RENT	BOUGHT	BUDGET	SPENT

Name:

ITEM	IDEAS	WHERE TO BUY/RENT	BOUGHT	BUDGET	SPENT

Name:

ITEM	IDEAS	WHERE TO BUY/RENT	BOUGHT	BUDGET	SPENT

Name:

ITEM	IDEAS	WHERE TO BUY/RENT	BOUGHT	BUDGET	SPENT

TO BUY

Name:					
ITEM	IDEAS	WHERE TO BUY/RENT	BOUGHT	BUDGET	SPENT

Name:					
ITEM	IDEAS	WHERE TO BUY/RENT	BOUGHT	BUDGET	SPENT

Name:					
ITEM	IDEAS	WHERE TO BUY/RENT	BOUGHT	BUDGET	SPENT

Name:					
ITEM	IDEAS	WHERE TO BUY/RENT	BOUGHT	BUDGET	SPENT

TO BUY

Name:

ITEM	IDEAS	WHERE TO BUY/RENT	BOUGHT	BUDGET	SPENT

Name:

ITEM	IDEAS	WHERE TO BUY/RENT	BOUGHT	BUDGET	SPENT

Name:

ITEM	IDEAS	WHERE TO BUY/RENT	BOUGHT	BUDGET	SPENT

Name:

ITEM	IDEAS	WHERE TO BUY/RENT	BOUGHT	BUDGET	SPENT

TO BUY

Name:					
ITEM	IDEAS	WHERE TO BUY/RENT	BOUGHT	BUDGET	SPENT

Name:					
ITEM	IDEAS	WHERE TO BUY/RENT	BOUGHT	BUDGET	SPENT

Name:					
ITEM	IDEAS	WHERE TO BUY/RENT	BOUGHT	BUDGET	SPENT

Name:					
ITEM	IDEAS	WHERE TO BUY/RENT	BOUGHT	BUDGET	SPENT

THE TO DOS

- [ ]
- [ ]
- [ ]
- [ ]
- [ ]
- [ ]
- [ ]
- [ ]
- [ ]
- [ ]
- [ ]
- [ ]
- [ ]
- [ ]
- [ ]
- [ ]
- [ ]
- [ ]
- [ ]
- [ ]
- [ ]
- [ ]
- [ ]
- [ ]
- [ ]
- [ ]
- [ ]
- [ ]
- [ ]
- [ ]

NOTES

IMPORTANT

THE TO DOS

NOTES

IMPORTANT

THE TO DOS

NOTES

IMPORTANT

THE TO DOS

NOTES

IMPORTANT

THE TO DOS

NOTES

IMPORTANT

THE TO DOS

NOTES

IMPORTANT

THE MONTHLY PLANNER

Month:

MONDAY	TUESDAY	WEDNESDAY	THURSDAY	FRIDAY	SATURDAY	SUNDAY

Month:

MONDAY	TUESDAY	WEDNESDAY	THURSDAY	FRIDAY	SATURDAY	SUNDAY

THE MONTHLY PLANNER

Month:

MONDAY	TUESDAY	WEDNESDAY	THURSDAY	FRIDAY	SATURDAY	SUNDAY

Month:

MONDAY	TUESDAY	WEDNESDAY	THURSDAY	FRIDAY	SATURDAY	SUNDAY

THE MONTHLY PLANNER

Month:

MONDAY	TUESDAY	WEDNESDAY	THURSDAY	FRIDAY	SATURDAY	SUNDAY

Month:

MONDAY	TUESDAY	WEDNESDAY	THURSDAY	FRIDAY	SATURDAY	SUNDAY

THE MONTHLY PLANNER

Month:

MONDAY	TUESDAY	WEDNESDAY	THURSDAY	FRIDAY	SATURDAY	SUNDAY

Month:

MONDAY	TUESDAY	WEDNESDAY	THURSDAY	FRIDAY	SATURDAY	SUNDAY

THE MONTHLY PLANNER

Month:

MONDAY	TUESDAY	WEDNESDAY	THURSDAY	FRIDAY	SATURDAY	SUNDAY

Month:

MONDAY	TUESDAY	WEDNESDAY	THURSDAY	FRIDAY	SATURDAY	SUNDAY

THE MONTHLY PLANNER

Month:

MONDAY	TUESDAY	WEDNESDAY	THURSDAY	FRIDAY	SATURDAY	SUNDAY

Month:

MONDAY	TUESDAY	WEDNESDAY	THURSDAY	FRIDAY	SATURDAY	SUNDAY

THE MONTHLY PLANNER

Month:

MONDAY	TUESDAY	WEDNESDAY	THURSDAY	FRIDAY	SATURDAY	SUNDAY

Month:

MONDAY	TUESDAY	WEDNESDAY	THURSDAY	FRIDAY	SATURDAY	SUNDAY

THE MONTHLY PLANNER

Month:						
MONDAY	TUESDAY	WEDNESDAY	THURSDAY	FRIDAY	SATURDAY	SUNDAY

Month:						
MONDAY	TUESDAY	WEDNESDAY	THURSDAY	FRIDAY	SATURDAY	SUNDAY

ENJOY!

We have reached the end of the Field Guide, my wedding planning Jedi Bridechillas and Groomchillas!

Whether this is your first wedding or your third, whether you're marrying a boy or a girl, whether it's a big event or small, your wedding will be a fantastic event because YOU planned it and you are marrying your special other person.

Being a Bridechilla is about maintaining focus and not being diverted by details and opinions that don't matter to you or your guests. Fuck chair covers and all the extra things that we get distracted by, but are ultimately meaningless.

You can't control other people or their behavior, and sometimes the silliness of it all, and the things that people make a big deal about, is ridiculous.

If someone has an absurd piece of advice or request that makes you want to punch a wall, don't get mad; deflect with humor, laughter and wine. Welcome the generosity and love of family and friends; they want to help you wherever they can but also don't feel obliged to do things their way because you think it's the 'right thing to do'. Find a balance. Find your voice and enjoy yourself.

Don't panic; breathe and be damn proud of yourselves for pulling this whole day together!

I'd love to meet you in The Bridechilla Community, our private Bridechilla Facebook Group, and be sure to subscribe to The Bridechilla Podcast.

Visit **thebridechilla.com** to find out more information that you can use in conjunction with this book for complete Bridechilla domination!

HAPPY DAYS

Aleisha
x

** Remember when it's all done and dusted to write thank you notes to your guests! **

A GOOD MARRIAGE IS ONE WHERE EACH PARTNER SECRETLY SUSPECTS THEY GOT THE BETTER DEAL.

Anonymous

The Maidchilla
Manual

GIVE YOUR BRIDESMAIDS THE GIFT OF CHILL

A Maidchilla is a chilled Bridesmaid who isn't fazed by dress drama, WhatsApp ghosting and inane power struggles. The *Maidchilla Manual* is the ultimate bridesmaid guide (and gift!), taking them through all of the events leading up to the wedding, and providing calming mantras and solutions to any potential 'people problems' that may come their way. Help your bridesmaids help you by gifting them a copy of the *Maidchilla Manual*.

The *Maidchilla Manual* features:

> Checklists and timelines of all potential pre-wedding events
> Party inspiration for bachelorette/hens, bridal showers
> Guidance to help your bridesmaids get in the Maidchilla mindset
> Helpful questions and tips to ensure smooth communication
> Each *Maidchilla Manual* comes with a complimentary "Will You Be My Maidchilla?" gift card

The *Maidchilla Manual* will show you how to be a bad-ass Bridesmaid, ditch the drama and get shit done!

Visit bridechillastore.com to get your copy. Happy Days!

The Bridechilla
Survival Guide

HOW TO PLAN THE WEDDING YOU WANT, DITCH WEDSTRESS, AND GET SHIT DONE

The *Bridechilla Survival Guide* helps you banish the wedding planning bullshit and takes you through all stages of wedding planning. Whether this is your first marriage or fourth, you will find wedding planning chill, value and guidance in these pages. The *Bridechilla Survival Guide* features real advice for real people on real budgets, and focuses on helping you navigate through the complicated stuff.

The *Bridechilla Survival Guide* will help you:

> Manage family dynamics, money and uninvited plus ones
> Celebrate that you are unique and your wedding should be too
> Use the Bridechilla secret weapon, The Fuck It Bucket, to change your wedding planning game
> Prioritize what you want vs what Pinterest and wedding magazines say you need
> Ditch the quest for perfection and instead plan an awesome, meaningful party

The *Bridechilla Survival Guide* empowers you to work as a team to create a wedding and marriage that goes the distance.

Visit **bridechillastore.com** to get your copy. **Happy Days!**

The Wedding Day Emergency Kit

BE CHILL: BE PREPARED FOR ANY EVENTUALITY

No matter how prepared and organized you may be, be on the safe side and pack the compact and very handy Bridechilla Wedding Day Emergency Kit. Being a Bridechilla is all about being prepared and ready to tackle any potential problem with calmness and chill. This wedding emergency pack is a discreet cosmetic bag and kit that contains helpful, travel-sized items that will guarantee to get you out of any last-minute preparation jams.

The Bridechilla Wedding Day Emergency Kit contains:

> Sewing kit
> Band-aid and blister pack
> Earring backs
> Bobby pins

> Comb and hairbrush
> Dental kit
> Vanity kit
> Double-sided tape

Complete with calming Bridechilla mantras and a delightful bag with two zip compartments for future use, the Bridechilla Wedding Day Emergency Kit is an ideal gift for brides and is a must-have item on your wedding planning to-do list!

Visit **bridechillastore.com** to get your copy. **Happy Days!**

The Bridechilla
Podcast

GIVE YOUR BRIDESMAIDS THE GIFT OF CHILL

Life's too short to be worrying about wedding favors, obligation guests, and bridesmaid dramas. *The Bridechilla Podcast* gives you practical guidance and support to help you plan a meaningful wedding celebration. Covering everything from planning timelines to mental health, family dynamics to body image, Bridechilla is bullshit-free and keeps it real.

Listen to *The Bridechilla Podcast*, the world's #1 wedding planning podcast that inspired the Bridechilla wedding planning guides. Join Bridechilla founder and host Aleisha as she interviews expert guests about making the process easier and have a laugh at the often complicated business of planning a wedding.

There are 400+ free episodes to download and listen to right now, including regular listener Q&A episodes. Search for and subscribe to *The Bridechilla Podcast* wherever you get your podcasts.

Visit **thebridechilla.com/podcast** to find out more. **Happy Days!**

ALEISHA MCCORMACK

Aleisha is an Australian comedian, podcaster and TV producer. She has worked as a writer and presenter for popular Australian comedy, panel and lifestyle programs, including Channel 10's *The Circle* and *The Project*.

Performing solo stand up comedy shows at international comedy festivals, Aleisha also toured the country with her one-woman show How To Get Rich, based on the adventures of meeting her husband Rich (they met on the internet and Aleisha flew across the world on a whim, from Melbourne to London, to meet him for the first time).

Rich and Aleisha got hitched in Melbourne in an intimate DIY wedding in 2012. Surprised by the level of A1 bullshit surrounding the wedding industry and additional pressure placed on couples to plan a "perfect day", Aleisha was inspired to start *The Bridechilla Podcast* to empower like-minded couples to plan their own wedding without losing their sanity.

Having produced hundreds of podcast episodes and built a community of free-thinking Bridechillas from all over the world, Aleisha is delighted and surprised that what she started has become a movement.

She currently resides in London with her current husband Rich, and her drink of choice is vodka, lime and soda. She's a reformed Nutella addict and her drunk party trick is doing the splits.

FUCK
PERFECT

Bridechilla Founder Aleisha McCormack